Flashing Daggers, Plagues, and Revenge:
Compelling Tales of Renaissance Florence

Cloaked assassins, conspiracies and murder most foul. The unscrupulous and the powerful, master works of art and ruling family patrons. Monolithic churches amidst Tuscan architectural wonders, sculptors, cardinals and painters, all conjuring household names — da Vinci, Michelangelo, Raphael, Machiavelli, and La Familia de' Medici.

Renaissance Florence comes alive in a superbly crafted and innovative collection of period accounts from storyteller and author Rona Commins in *True Tales of Italian Intrigue*.

Commins' work evokes fascinating images of Florence over two centuries of the Italian Renaissance period, bolstered by skillfully drawn historical sketches. Designed to offer modern tourists who visit the city's piazzas (central squares) visual treats for their minds' eyes, each story unfolds in such a way that with Commins' volume in hand, one can literally stand in each piazza and hear the conspiratorial whispers, witness the grotesque carnage of Italian vengeance, and absorb the bedazzling beauty of Florentine art and architecture.

The stories are impeccably researched, thoroughly documented, and compellingly written. Some tales are relayed through first person narration, giving the book enough 'real life' flavoring that the reader can actually savor the romance and intrigue that characterized the Florentine Republic of half a millennium ago.

One need not travel to Italy to relish Commins' work . . . it is the sort of read that one enjoys at the end of the day, snuggled safely in bed, ready to face the black plague, or feel the dagger thrusts of Medici revenge, or soak in the breathtaking beauty of the wealthiest palazzos while Latin chants waft softly across the cobbled streets. But if a trip to Florence is in the making, *True Tales of Italian Intrigue* is an essential companion.

> — Alan E. Waite
> Author of *Hats . . . How Felt Can Save America*,
> lecturer, Adjunct Professor, WWII Historian, American Civil War Guide
> & Historian and CEO of Praxis Corporation

An indispensable guide to finding concerts in Florence, this book will give you instant information for finding music in many different and unexpected locations, some of them free . . . and all in walking distance within Florence.

> — Barbara Baker DMus
> Indiana University, Blog: http://onopera.com

Twenty-four consecutive years as a teacher in Florence for the California State Universities of Sacramento and San Francisco has presented Rona Commins with the opportunity to discover little-known tales of Renaissance Florence and to develop her skill as a story teller. Year after year she has lured travelers to return to Italy a second and even a third time to hear and see it through her eyes. Rona Commins is the most in-demand teacher we have had the pleasure of hosting at ACCENT International Educational Consortium Centers in Florence, Paris, London and Madrid.

> — Ray Vernon, Director, ACCENT International

Slip through time and into Florence's past with Rona Commins' stories which bring to life the assassination of a Medici brother, jousting in Piazza Santa Croce, a plague funeral procession, and a bridegroom rushing to meet his intended. Numerous quotes from ancient texts add authentic voices to this fascinating stroll through history. Addresses and visiting hours to sites mentioned in the stories are an added bonus, and make this book not only a collection of short stories, but also a valuable guide to the must-see sites of Florence.

— Kathleen Ann Gonzalez
Author of *Seductive Venice: In Casanova's Footsteps*

Unknown to me were the people and places in this book . . . Florence, Italy is a place I have visited only casually flipping through the pages of a magazine . . . the author evoked my appetite by the display of greed, loyalty, betrayal, political maneuvering and unyielding ambition, all the elements of which run through every land, every place and every gathering of people.

Florence Italy is one of the worlds most renowned cities. Rona Commins transcends her role into a docent who takes the reader on a virtual tour which awakens a sense of true passion and fabric of Italian life. Embracing this literary landscape has invigorated my sense of history, passion, ambiance and spirit of the Renaissance.

— Andréa L. Williams
Publisher and CEO of *MotherWit* Magazine and Consulting
Editor of *Dominion Magazines* Family & Children Department

This is a fascinating read for anyone interested in the culture of Florence.

— Craig Kubey
Author of *The Viet Vet Survival Guide*
and co-author of *Pat Summerall's Sports in America*

to- Kayli
Here are new stories for you!

FOREVER

Florence

TRUE TALES OF
ITALIAN INTRIGUE

*A Collection of Short Stories
& Guide to Concerts*

RONA COMMINS

*International voice Instructor
Tour Guide • Adjunct Professor & Lecturer*

Rona Commins

We want to hear from you ... please send your questions
and stories of how this book enhanced your tour through the "history
behind the history" of Florence Italy to

ronacommins@yahoo.com
(916) 487-2137
Sacramento, California

Forever Florence
  True Tales of Italian Intrigue
  A Collection of Short Stories and Musical Guide

Copyright © 2014 by Rona Commins

True Tales of Italian Intrigue ISBN 9780990474609
Library of Congress Cataloguing in Publication Data

Rona Commins, 1940-
    Forever Florence – True Tales of Italian Intrigue.
    Includes bibliographical references and index
    1. Renaissance Florence—Non-fiction short stories. 2. Florence (Italy)—History
1400-1600—Non-fiction short stories. 3. Nobility—Italy—Florence—Non-fiction short
stories. 4. Florence (Italy)—Guide book—Non-fiction short stories. 5. Florence
(Italy)—Music concert guide.
I. Title

Library of Congress Control Number: 2014911443

Cover Design & Photograph: Mary L. Chapeau
Interior Photography: Maggie Suckow & Rona Commins
Interior Book Design & Production: Chapeau Graphic Design & Publishing
Illustrations: Mary L. Chapeau
Fonts: Clearface, Avant garde, Modified Gothic and Modified Edwardian Script

For

Richard Commins

View of Florence from the balcony of San Miniato al Monte.

Contents

Rona Commins at the Benedictine Monastery gift shop, in front of the church of San Miniato al Monte.

Prologue

"What city, not merely in Italy, but in all the world, is more securely placed within its circle of walls, more proud in its palazzi, more bedecked with churches, more beautiful in its architecture, more imposing in its gates, richer in piazzas, happier in its wide streets, greater in its people, more glorious in its citizenry, more inexhaustible in wealth, more fertile in its fields?"

— Coluccio Salutati — 1406

"The country of Italy is the most intellectual part of the world; Tuscany is the most intellectual part of Italy; and Florence is the most intellectual city in Tuscany."

— San Bernardino of Siena — 1444

"Florence is considered the finest and most beautiful city — not only in Christendom, but in the entire world.

— Giovanni Rucellai — 1470

True Tales of Italian Intrigue is the story of Florence in the 1400s and 1500s. Florence was one of the largest cities in Europe, larger than Rome or London; its 1490 population of 75,000 made it comparable to Venice, Milan, Naples, or Paris. Its gigantic arc of forty-foot-tall walls extended for five continuous miles, broken by forty-five seventy-foot-high watch towers and eleven guarded gates. To a pilgrim from Paris on the way to Rome, coming into town from across the Alps and down from the Apennines, the city spread into view covered in the shadow of the newest and largest-in-the-world dome of the Catholic Church, the Cathedral of Santa Maria del Fiore, 'Saint Mary of the Flowers,' named after the town's ancient Roman title of Florentia.

From the north, visitors arrive in the city center of Palazzo della Signoria (now Palazzo Vecchio, 'old palace') by way of the largest street in town, Via Larga (now Via Cavour.) Many new private palaces have been built in the city, over thirty of them in fifty years. The palace takes the name of the family which built it; the largest is on Via Larga, the Palazzo Medici. The Medici family has furnished de facto rulers of Florence for almost two centuries. Florence stands in the center of the province and dominates most of Tuscany and the valley of the Arno River. Fifty miles inland from the sea at Pisa, the Arno is navigable upriver almost to the gates of Florence which has made the city a very important center for business, factories, commerce, and banking.

A family palace is a business place with a showroom for merchandise on the ground floor. In the home of a cloth merchant, there are bolts of cloth in many colors, with camphor and salts in pomades suspended from the ceiling to keep away moths. Upstairs is the owner's studiolo where business records are stored. There are desks, tables to count money, coin caskets, chests, shelves and cupboards for documents, accounting books, bundles of letters, weighing scales, maps. Private treasures stored here include collections of antique coins and medals. A wealthy owner will buy a pair of spectacles which he will keep here.

The largest room in the house is on the *piano nobile*, the second floor. A spacious hall looking onto the street, it contains a long table used for formal occasions and family gatherings. Women watch processions from the windows; the family congregates around the fireplace in the winter. There are multicolored brocades, velvets and damasks: bright carpets are draped over tables, chairs, and window seats, family wealth too precious to be placed on the floor. Walls are painted with frescos and murals and in the winter, hung with tapestries to keep out the cold.

The elaborately carved bed in the master bedroom is the most expensive object in the house. Mulberry leaves may be scattered underneath to attract fleas from mattresses and bolsters. Activities based around the bed include birth, sickness and death, all of which take place semi-publicly. Chests or *cassoni*, are prized wedding gifts which hold the most precious goods here, in the safest room in the house: family linens and jewels. A devotional work for daily prayers is kept in the master bedroom, an image of the Madonna or Christ either painted or carved, usually in a niche in the wall or on a prie-dieu. The open-air loggia of the top floor is used to take fresh air and hang the laundry. The most modern palaces have an adjoining bathroom with metal bathtub with warm water brought down from the top-floor kitchen.

Florence is bustling with trade and manufacturing. The Arno turns the mills and provides water for washing and dying wool, a business which is carried out all along the river. The second bridge down from the Ponte Vecchio is Ponte alla Carraia where carts cross the river carrying wool to the parish of San Frediano where it is spun and woven into cloth. An important banking city, Florence's wealthy merchant families have done business for generations throughout Europe to Kings and Popes.

The exciting new science of printing has brought the books of Italian writers Dante, Boccaccio, and Petarch to more and more people; this enhances Florence's reputation abroad and spreads the Tuscan dialect which will become the language of Italy. Boccaccio's *Decameron* records the aftermath of the Black Death; Petrarch writes the poetry of love; Giovanni Villani tells of life in Florence in his *Florentine Chronicle*; Leon Battista Alberti composes treatises on painting and architecture; Machiavelli tells of the machinations of rulers to maintain political control.

The city of Florence contains over fifty piazzas or squares, the majority of which serve as backdrops to the main churches. They are the open spaces in a Renaissance city where public spectacle can occur. I have chosen to focus my stories on piazzas so that the reader can stand in front of a historic monument, look around himself, and see the stories happening before his eyes. Volume I begins with the three piazzas that any visitor to Florence will see on any journey: Piazza del Duomo, Piazza della Signoria, and Piazza Santa Croce. I have also included one more that may make you say, "I have never seen that piazza" – Piazza Santissima Annunziata.

The ten stories here are only the beginning of the tales which can be told about this fascinating city where the Renaissance began. It is exciting to stand in Florence, and to know that the venues of the "Tales" are still there to be discovered. The stones under Michelangelo's feet are the stones under your feet. Furnished palaces are there, ancient city gates and walls still stand, the Roman forum and colosseum are visible beneath the crust of ages. The giant keys to the gates of Florence, Ghirlandaio's suite of frescos in a family chapel, Dante's baptismal font, all are there for YOU to discover. Come and discover them with me in this continuing series: True Tales of Italian Intrigue.

Chapter One

Murder In The Cathedral

*"Florence's gigantic dome is "a structure so immense, so
steeply rising towards the sky, that it covers all Tuscan people
with its shadow."*

> — Leon Battista Alberti
> 1436 *Delle Pitture*

"Politics have no relations to morals."

> — Nicolo Machiavelli
> 1511 *Il Principe*

26 April 1478, Easter

Giuliano de'Medici lay splayed on the icy marble floor, covered in the gore of nineteen stab wounds. It was thought by the assassins that even today he might not have been at church at all, and all the plans for the overthrow of the Medici who had ruled Florence for nearly a half century would come to nothing.

The deed had been planned for the previous week at a banquet in the Medici family villa on the hill near Fiesole.[1] Poison would be dropped into a cup with a hinged cover, traditionally used to thwart any attempt at assassination by poison. When the gilded cover was closed it would be brought to the table: two ostrich-shell cups, two deaths, two Medici co-ruling brothers dispatched.[2] There would have been no need for the nasty bloodying of Giuliano's red and black tights or knee-length red cloak, fashionable clothing perfect for the warm days of the budding Florence spring.

But Giuliano had been ill and hadn't attended the banquet last week. Even today he might not arrive for the solemn High Mass of Easter in Santa Maria del Fiore, Florence's Cathedral. The Pazzi family was ready to strike: the Medici and Pazzi banking families had declared themselves to be mortal enemies since the Pope had shifted

Marble angels from della Robbia's Cantoria *seem to be singing a final* te deum *over the dead body of Giuliano de' Medici.*

his banking from the Medici family bank to the Pazzi family bank. With papal gold in Pazzi hands, wresting political power would be the next Pazzi goal. But with the illness of Giuliano, things had taken an unexpected turn at the Medici banquet. Murdering one Medici brother would leave the other to rule and to wreak family reparations on the Pazzi to the end of time.

Up to this point in the Easter holiday, the Pazzi family had been following family tradition. The Pazzi in Florence were always important at Easter time. Every child in town had learned the story of how the knight, Pazzino de' Pazzi, had scaled the walls of Jerusalem in the First Crusade:

In June of 1097 Pazzino lay camped beneath the walls of the great city of Jerusalem, the holiest of all cities, the strongest fortress in the world. His metal armor roasted him by day and discomfited him by night, but he was prepared for this siege of the infidels! He had seen Constantinople, a hundred times greater than his own native Florence. He had paid reverence to the "Holy Relics:" the Crown of Thorns; the Hair of John the Baptist; the Mantle of Elijah. Pazzino was hot and dusty from walking thousands of miles across deserts, hungry and thirsty from encountering ravaged villages and poisoned wells, but he was going in! History declared that in 1097, Pazzino de' Pazzi was first over the walls of Jerusalem in the First Crusade.

Every Easter Sunday since the First Crusade, the Pazzi family had been rewarded with the honor and the duty to strike the "holy fire" in the Florentine church of Santi Apostoli[3] with flints brought from the Church of the Holy Sepulcher in Jerusalem. Citizens lined the streets to the Cathedral to watch the procession as Pazzi, clerics, and city officials carried torches to celebrate *Scoppio del Carro*,[4] the annual Easter celebration at Florence Cathedral. The fiery paper dove would fly on its wire from the Cathedral altar to the Baptistery, resting for only seconds upon a nest of fireworks. Then a multi-colored conflagration of sparks would soar above the Baptistery to light the whole Piazza del Duomo like a million fireflies!

Easter in 1478 was particularly beautiful. The early spring that year had brought out the flowers and herbs used to festoon the white oxen which led the procession to the Cathedral. Botticelli, watching the procession with his artist's eyes, must have transferred this image with brush and tempera when he created the flowers of Flora in *Primavera* and the *Birth of Venus* to hang on the walls of the Medici summer villa of Castello. These secular images of mythological subjects were not meant to be seen except by the non-prudish eyes of Medici and invited guests.[5]

But in Florence on April 25, 1478, politics were afoot. Who would murder two brothers of the ruling political family in the Cathedral, tomorrow on Easter Sunday at High Mass, with the eyes of thousands of congregants raised to the elevation of the Host. Francesco de' Pazzi would love to undo a lifetime of jealousy watching blood spurt from the sword's hilt in the first deep joyous thrust into a Medici breast. But the chosen assassin, the papal mercenary Count Montesecco, had more scruples and premonition of how the future could unravel, and refused to spill blood in that sacred place and time. The conscription of two less-scrupulous priests made it a foursome with Francesco de' Pazzi and fellow banker Bernardo Bandini Baroncelli, who together became the chosen hit men for this 15th century act of Italian political intrigue, the assassination of the Medici brothers.

PHOTO BY: Rona Commins

Left sacristy doors with organ loft, the sacristy where Lorenzo escaped to save his life.

Dante holding a copy of his Divine Comedy.

The next morning, Sunday 26 April, Giuliano was still home ill. People were arriving in the Cathedral in clumps, women were congregating and standing in the nave on the left side (*sinistra*) and men on the right (*dextra*).[6] It was an important day in Florence, not only because of the Easter holiday, but because of two visitors, the Cardinal of San Giorgio and the Archbishop of Pisa. No one saw the armed men waiting inside the city. Montesecco had arrived with "thirty mounted crossbowmen and fifty foot soldiers, all as beautifully attired and handsome as any company that had ever been seen, claiming that they had come from Imola to accompany Pope Sixtus's nephew, [the Cardinal of San Giorgio] back to Rome."[7]

The Cathedral was packed now, and Giuliano was as yet nowhere to be seen. Francesco de' Pazzi and Bernardo Baroncelli walked the few blocks back up the Via Larga, the widest street in Florence, to the Medici brothers' home at Palazzo Medici. Giuliano had probably planned to celebrate a quiet Sunday Mass in the private home chapel frescoed by Benozzo Gozzoli. In the chapel, he could bask in the sight of Medici family members accompanying the gilded Gozzoli *Procession of the Magi*[8] and escape today's Easter crowds. What convincing words about "Easter Holiday" and "maintaining the family image" Francesco and Bernardo must have used to lead Giuliano the few blocks to the Cathedral and to his own execution.[9] History records that the first blow was struck by Baroncelli with the words "Here, traitor!"[10] Francesco followed Baroncelli's blow with such a frenzied succession of stabs that the official count was twenty, nineteen for Giuliano with the twentieth a cut by Francesco to his own thigh.

The two sacrilegious priests meantime, wielding swords and bucklers, had been busy with their own attempted assassination of Giuliano's older brother, Lorenzo. Destined to be known to the world as *il Magnifico*, Lorenzo was maybe luckier, maybe a little more alert, maybe a little more older-brother-worldly-wise. Wrapping his cape around his left arm as a shield, with his short sword in his right hand, he was able to parry thrusts and elude the two priests, suffering only a slight wound to the neck. Lorenzo, as a noble, stood behind the rood screen of the octagonal choir, to the right near the south sacristy door beneath Donatello's *Cantoria*.[11] He jumped over the low wooden railing of the choir, crossed the large music stand and the altar, and escaped into the north sacristy.[12] Accompanying friends bolted the bronze della Robbia doors after him.

Lorenzo probably never saw Giuliano, lying in the shadows farther away to the left of the choir, the red of gore blending with the red short cape and the red and black bi-colored stockings. The attractive, elegant and kind Giuliano was four years younger than Lorenzo and held a special place in the hearts of Florentines. Only three years earlier at the age of twenty-two, Giuliano had taken part in a joust in Piazza Santa Croce. Distinguished guests attended from all over Italy, arriving in costumes and armor never before seen in Florence. Giuliano had been most elegant of all in his fashionable *bella figura*[13] coat of silver armor, helmet and standard. Giuliano hired the best metal artist in the city to design his equipage, the young Andrea del Verrocchio, whose fountain *Boy with a Dolphin*[14] had just been placed in the garden of Palazzo Medici.

The cavernous space of the Cathedral was quickly deserted as politicians and ambassadors, priests and servants, women and children all fled for the doors to find refuge in neighboring houses or shops. The bells of the Palazzo della Signoria were soon sounding the alarm and all the parishes of Tuscany resounded with bells echoing the warning.

PHOTO BY: Maggie Suckow

della Robbia's Cantoria which was in place above the north sacristy when Giuliano was mudered

Francesco de' Pazzi, bleeding from his wounded thigh, dragged himself around the back of the Cathedral a few blocks to the safety of the Pazzi Palace,[15] probably thinking all the way "Now all of Florence will rise against the anarchy of the Medici!"

Lorenzo remained in the sacristy with those who had escaped with him, wondering when it would be safe to exit, and asking constantly about his brother. His friend Segismondo della Stufa climbed up the spiral staircase which led from the sacristy to della Robbia's cantoria to see who or what remained outside the bolted doors. Below him, della Stufa could see Giuliano, definitely dead. The picture of Dante, a fresco recently completed by Domenico Michelino, seemed to stare solemnly down from the wall. Dante held a copy of his *Divine Comedy* and appeared to be predicting two centuries after his death that this family feud should be assigned to a "canto" of his *Inferno*. Standing above in the Cantoria, della Stufa could imagine that della Robbia's white carrara marble choir boys were singing a final *te deum* that echoed mournfully round and round in the white-plastered inverted-egg of Brunelleschi's dome.[16]

The murder of Giuliano shocked Florence, not at all the result which the Pazzi expected. Instead of rallying behind the Pazzi, the enraged Florentines pursued the conspirators and took to the streets to defend the Republic. The crowd went on a hunt for the assassins who had escaped from the cathedral toward nearby Piazza della Signoria where they had expected to be joined by rebellious Florentines. As Pazzi partisans attempted to seize the government, Lorenzo resumed control. Lorenzo and the whole of Florence took retribution on the Pazzi clan, a retribution which took a full ten years to its completion.

A native Florentine, Machiavelli,[17] nine years old at the time, could not help but store in the archives of his mind what he witnessed in this attempted political takeover: Pazzi were tossed from windows, thrown in the Arno river, dragged naked through the streets. It could not help but shape his thinking as he wrote his greatest work, *The Prince*, which influenced generations of states and statesmen with its premise "the end justifies the means." *The Prince* would be used for centuries as a manual of how a cunning ruler should govern.

Lorenzo, the future and forever *Magnifico*, would begin to reinvigorate the rule of the Medici in Florence and wreak retribution upon the attempting usurpers.

All times given here for opening and closing of museums, churches, etc. are in 24 hour time. After 12:00 noon subtract 12 hours from the time quoted.

1. The Medici Villa may be reached from Fiesole by walking south down the hill toward San Domenico on Via Vecchia Fiesolana, a narrow street located in the southwestern corner of the main square. The Villa is on the left, surrounded by walls with the Medici *stemma* (shield) on the gate. Not open to the public unless a group arrangement is made in advance. To go to Fiesole from Florence, take bus #7 from Piazza San Marco.

2. Medici dining and decorative accoutrements and the family jewel collection may be seen at Palazzo Pitti. Open daily 8:15-18:30, and to 19:30 June-August. ....Closed first and last Mondays of the month. Cumulative ticket #2 includes Bóboli Gardens, Costume Gallery, and Porcelain Museum.

3. The church of Santi Apostoli is one of the oldest churches in the city. According to an inscription on the façade, it was founded by Charlemagne in 786 but actually dates from 1075. Piazza del Limbo lies lower than the street and is named after a cemetery for unbaptised infants who died in original sin.
Santi Apostoli ....Piazza del Limbo off Borgo SS Apostoli
Open 8:00-10:00 and 16:00-19:00

4. *Scoppio del Carro* is still celebrated every Easter Sunday in Florence. Florence hearth fires were lit with the "holy fire" to guarantee a good harvest, stable civic life and good business for the coming year. Botticelli's paintings *Primavera* and *Birth of Venus* may be viewed at:
Uffizi Gallery...Piazzale degli Uffizi 1
Open Tues-Sun 8:15-18:50, closed Mon

5. Previous to this time, commissions came mainly from the church and were for religious subjects. Even when the subject was secular, history, or myth, clothed bodies were traditional. The Medici were breaking new ground with *The Birth of Venus* and *Primavera* which were commissioned for a bedroom at the villa and not intended to be seen by the public.

6. Congregants at a Catholic Mass would stand (there were no seats) looking toward the altar which was behind a rood screen, hidden from their view. Inside the screen would be the altar, the choir stalls and a single large music stand to hold the choir hymnal. In Florence Cathedral there was an octagonal area, still visible in the marble of the floor, surrounded by an octagonal railing. A visual representation of the Pazzi assassination exists in a commemorative medal, commissioned from the artist Bertoldo di Giovanni by Lorenzo a few months after the murder. It may be seen in the Bargello. After Vatican II in 1959, most remaining rood screens were torn down, and Catholic masses are celebrated facing the congregants in the language of the people instead of Latin. A rood screen may be seen in Florence in Santa Maria del Carmine, in Venice in Chiesa dei Frari and San Marco, and in Chartres Cathedral in France.
Bargello, National Sculpture Gallery ....Via del Proconsolo 4
Open Tues-Sat, April-Oct 8:15-16:50
Nov-March 8:15-13:50 (also 1st, 3rd, 5th Mon and 2nd, 4th Sun of month)

7. *April Blood* by Lauro Martines, p.114.

8. Gozzoli's *Procession of the Magi* may be seen in the chapel of
Palazzo Medici-Ricardi...Via Cavour 3
Open daily 9:00-19:00, closed Wed

9. The assassins would have been lucky that they did not make an attempt on Giuliano's life in the chapel of Palazzo Medici-Ricardi. Gozzoli's chapel was built with thick double walls which offered secret escape routes and hiding places.

10. Martines p.116.

11. A *Cantoria* is a raised singing gallery or choir loft. Della Robbia and Donatello's *Cantorie* may be seen in the museum Opera del Duomo. Both were actually organ lofts installed after the 1436 dedication of the Duomo. Della Robbia's was for a new organ on the left over the door of the north sacristy, Donatello's was on the right for the restoration of the existing organ.
Opera del Duomo, temporarily closed for restoration in 2014 ....Piazza del Duomo 9
Open Mon-Sat 9:00-19:30
Sun 9:00-13:40

12. A *sacristy* is a room where the priests' vestments and chalices, wine and wafers for the mass are stored.
Duomo, Santa Maria del Fiore Cathedral ....Piazza del Duomo 9
Open Mon-Sat 9:00-19:30
Sun 9:00-13:40

13. *Bella figura* translates "to make a good showing," always to be properly dressed and groomed before stepping out the door, and always to say the proper thing in social situations. "Their suits, their shirts, their ties, their shoes, their haircuts, even their fingernails were all beyond perfection." Wikipedia.

14. Verrocchio's *Boy with a Dolphin* can be seen in the courtyard fountain of Palazzo Vecchio. The courtyard of Palazzo Vecchio is always open and lighted.

15. The Pazzi Palace is on the corner of Via del Proconsolo and Via degli Albizzi. The Pazzi *stemma* (coat-of-arms) has been restored to its place on the façade. (Not open to view)

16. The dome had not yet been frescoed. On Easter in 1478 it was still painted the original base coat of white. The intention was for the Cathedral dome to be covered with mosaics like the Baptistery dome, but when finally completed it was frescoed by Vasari in the less expensive medium of paint.

17. Machiavelli was a writer and historian. A negotiator admired for his diplomacy, he became an ambassador to Rome, France, and Germany. Barbara Hodgson, *Italy Out of Hand*, p.98

The little Loggia of the Bigallo where abandoned children were placed to wait to be adopted.

Chapter Two

Return Of The Black Plague

"Neither a doctor's advice nor the strength of medicine could do anything to cure this disease....everyone felt he was doomed to die and, as a result, abandoned his property, so that most of the houses had become common property, and any stranger who came upon them used them as if he were their rightful owner."

"So many corpses would arrive in front of a church every day that . . . when all the graves were full, huge trenches were dug in all the cemeteries of the churches and into them the new arrivals were dumped by the hundreds; and they were packed in there with dirt, one on top of another, like a ship's cargo, until the trench was filled."

> — Giovanni Boccaccio
> 1350 *Decameron*

"Poverty is easy prey to wealth and....wealth accompanied by prudence will accomplish anything it desires without censure."

> — Giorgio Vasari
> 1568 *Lives of the Artists*

11 January 1494

On this day in the year 1494, the artist Domenico di Tommaso di Currado Bigordi, commonly known as Ghirlandaio,[1] died of the plague in his forty-fifth year.

The funeral procession wound like a long black snake, slithering slowly through the narrow streets of Florence. A whole mournful procession ventured on foot, on horse, and in carriages, following the trail past Piazza del Duomo to Santa Maria Novella. It was the Black Plague returned, and only the loss of one of their native sons and greatest artists whom they had watched at work could make a Florentine willing to trail behind the black bier.

Five years ago, in 1489, the biggest excitement in Florence was watching the Ghirlandaio brothers paint in the church of Santa Maria Novella.[2] It took a little time to get to the church, on the outskirts of Florence, but it was well worth the effort. As each layer of wet plaster *intonaco*[3] was laid down and painted, we could see people we knew appearing on the wall, from Tornabuoni family members to city officials, and who knew, maybe even ourselves! This was why everyone in Florence went to watch when a Ghirlandaio painting was in process. The rich banker, Giovanni Tornabuoni, had asked Ghirlandaio to paint scenes of the Virgin Mary and John the Baptist, but Tornabuoni knew that he would see portraits of his beautiful daughter and her friends inside a richly furnished Florentine home. Including people he knew in his art was a Ghirlandaio trademark, part of his success.

Ghirlandaio had always sketched since he was a boy, drawing the faces and bodies of passersby as he sat in front of his father's gold smith shop. As the oldest son in the family, he was supposed to follow his father's trade, but he loved to draw people! This gave Ghirlandaio a unique advantage, for portraiture became a signature trait in his work as a fresco painter of large and involved scenes. No one but Ghirlandaio would have thought of fitting the Medici sons into a scene by depicting them walking up stairs in front of a fresco full of twenty-seven other portraits placed in an architectural setting of Piazza Signoria![4]

The Santa Maria Novella commission was enormous. Would Ghirlandaio be able to complete frescoes on the huge walls, design three stained glass windows, and paint a free-standing altarpiece front and back in the time stipulated by his patron? An individual artist could take years to complete such a commission, and the gossip was that the Tornabuoni contract allowed four years.

Ghirlandaio had a reputation for being able to lay down wet plaster and paint it faster than anybody else in Florence. He had created an organized and efficient *bottega*[5] with workers scurrying around him, tamping drawings on underwalls, laying down

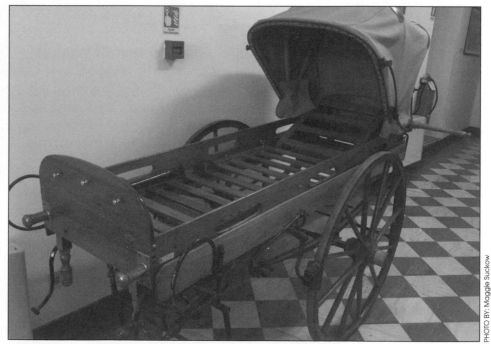

PHOTO BY: Maggie Suckow

The hand cart used by the Confraternita della Misericordia volunteers to pick up sick victims of the Black Plague.

wet plaster, and mixing the colors. Ghirlandaio himself would paint the portrait of Tornabuoni's daughter visiting at the birth of Mary, his brothers would be above on the scaffolding working on the less conspicuous scenes of the life of the Virgin Mary, and assistants would be assigned to fill in with trees, flowers, vases, etc. Ghirlandaio must have benefited from observing the della Robbia family organization whose *bottega* would gain commissions year after year for ceramic religious art, produced *en masse* less expensively in clay than it would cost in wood or marble.[6] Now anyone in Florence can afford a family Madonna which is both beautiful and a genuine work of art

When the Black Plague first appeared in our city in 1348, three-fifths of the population of 100,000 people died; in Europe Florence was called "the city of plague." So many died that there was almost no one left to pick up corpses, so they remained smelly in their beds. Trenches were dug at every church as wide and deep as the parish was large. Almost none, or very few, were cured. All the shops were shut, taverns closed; only the apothecaries and the churches remained open. Homes were left unlocked and there was no one daring enough to touch anything because it seemed that things remained poisoned and that whoever used them picked up the illness.

Now in 1489, people knew enough to be on their guard. The safest strategy was to leave for a country villa if you had one. If not, stay inside and NEVER enter a space with the plague; even dogs and chickens died![7] The anonymous volunteers of the *Misericordia* were the courageous people who transported the sick and the dying, picking up the live ones in baskets to carry them to the hospital and stacking up the dead ones in carts bound for the church cemetery. The volunteers' long black robes with cowl and mask seemed to protect them from disease, and it certainly protected their identity from superstitious and fearful citizens.

The *Confraternita della Misericordia*[8] has been in the same building for over 200 years, in a useful location nestled next to the Duomo and the Campanile. It is a place you can go if you are in need of quiet, a private and cool place to pray on a hot summer day. Stepping up the stairs from the street by the Cathedral and pushing through the black curtains of the chapel, you can forget that crowds are shopping around the corner in Via de' Calzaiuoli. Just across the street in the *Compagnia di Santa Maria del Bigallo*[9] in the little loggia, lost and abandoned children are placed to wait, watch, and hope to be adopted into a family. In school, when we were studying the writings of our great poet Dante, we came here to the Bigallo to see what Florence looked like five hundred years ago in the fresco painting when there was no Duomo towering over the city. We saw instead the earliest church of Santa Reparata with many old houses around it.

It may have been the volunteers of the *Misericordia* who prepared the body of Ghirlandaio for his burial. I'm not sure of that, for he had many friends in the city and was hired by wealthy bankers, wool dealers, and cloth and gold merchants. It was good and right that he should be buried in Santa Maria Novella and not clear across town in the great memorial church of Santa Croce which is dedicated to Saint Francis.

The clothing worn by the Misericordia volunteers when assisting victims of the Black Plague.

PHOTO BY: Maggie Suckow

Ghirlandaio will be much happier here where he painted Mary of Santa Maria del Fiore, and John the Baptist of the Baptistery, the two saints of his beloved Florence.

It was a shock, as it always is, when the funeral procession entered Santa Maria Novella and we saw Masaccio's *Trinity* directly in front of our eyes. Truly it stopped people in their tracks when they first saw it barely more than sixty years ago. Masaccio painted in a way which taught all our moderns: so realistic, so perfectly three dimensional, you could step through its door, past the kneeling donors, and into the space of the Father, Son, and Holy Ghost extending deep into the interior. Masaccio's *Trinity* is open to everyone's view in the public nave of the church while Ghirlandaio's masterpiece, now that it is finished, is concealed behind the rood screen and the altar, seen only by a few churchmen, the choir, and the nobility.[10]

The frescoes of Masaccio and Ghirlandaio are so different, yet so alike! Masaccio's *Trinity* had no mathematical basis for measurement; he created it solely through natural talent and eye. Ghirlandaio's perspectives are designed on a very elaborate achitectural plan, but also created by eye alone, without the use of mathematics. Truly in 1494 we live in the time of the greatest artists!

There was such a scandal about the rights to the chapel behind the altar that it almost continued to this day. This particular chapel in Santa Maria Novella is in a very prestigious location behind the altar, almost as desired a chapel as one in the Cathedral. The rights belonged to the Sassetti family and Francesco Sassetti's intentions were to have Ghirlandaio paint scenes of his family with his patron saint, Saint Francis of Assisi. But Santa Maria Novella was a Dominican church, a rival of the Franciscan order, and in no way would the Dominicans allow the most prominent location in their church to be used to glorify the founder of the rival Franciscan order.

It took many years of a lawsuit between the Dominicans and the Sassetti before legal backing was given to the Dominicans, and the Sassetti family finally angrily withdrew from their plans. Ghirlandaio still had the painting contract with the Sassetti, but the plans for the frescoes of the life of Saint Francis were transferred to the church of Santa Trinitá on Via Tornabuoni, a street of the nobles in Florence, near the Arno River.

Tornabuoni wanted the chapel behind the altar in Santa Maria Novella for his family chapel, but it took a bit of Italian intrigue and some skillful maneuvering on his part to gain the right of patronage. The rights had first belonged to the Ricci family, even before the Sassetti. The Ricci were a wealthy family which had become impoverished and could not afford to renew the hundred-year-old frescoes of Andrea Orcagna. At a ceremonial meeting of the chapter the brothers transferred the rights from the Ricci to the Sassetti, who had the means to renew them. The brothers were tired of performing the Holy Sacrament of the Lord before such outdated, flaking and peeling frescoes.

But now that the Sassetti and their Saint Francis were out of the way, the Ricci renewed their claim. Tornabuoni was morally if not legally responsible to the Ricci. He wrote a contract that satisfied the Ricci family: he agreed to pay for the whole project himself, and he would put the Ricci family coat-of-arms in the "most honorable and prominent place" in the chapel.

Everyone in the nave could hear the commotion when the whole Ricci clan came into Santa Maria Novella and said they could not find their coat-of-arms. Ghirlandaio had painted the Ricci *stemma*[11] barely visible, while Tornabuoni's coat-of-arms was large and very prominent. Tornabuoni explained, "There it is, in the frame of the altar painting," a position "close to the Holy Sacrament" and therefore "the most honorable and prominent place." Who could argue?

Ghirlandaio painted in *buon fresco*, a technique he and very few others had perfected. The wet tempera in each area of intonaco was completed upon first application, all in one go, and did not require added touch-ups with tempera paints after the work was finished. It was one of the pleasures of watching Ghirlandaio at work, and especially so in his masterpiece in the Tornabuoni Chapel. We also were able to watch there a new and most amazingly gifted apprentice at work, a thirteen-year-old boy named Michelangelo Buonarotti.

1. The name **Ghirlanadio** was a family nick-name. Father Tommaso Bigordi was a goldsmith famed for creating a garland-like necklace of gold worn by Florentine women.

2. **Santa Maria Novella**   **Spanish Chapel**
   Piazza Santa Maria Novella   Cloister to the left of the church
   Open Mon-Thurs 9:00-17:30   Open Mon-Thurs & Sat 9:00-17:00
   Fri 11:00-17:30   Closed Fri & Sun
   Sat 9:00-17:00
   Sun 13:00-17:00

   Farmacia Santa Maria Novella, apothecary shop founded 1221,
   sells toiletries and medicinal herbs.   Via della Scala 16
   Open daily 9:00-20:00
   Museum 10:30-19:00

3. *Intonoco* is the wet plaster applied to a surface which will be painted with a water-based color used in fresco painting. When dry, the color becomes a permanent part of the plaster.

4. Ghirlandaio's *The Confirmation of the Rule* is in the **Sassetti Chapel.**
   Santa Trinita   Piazza S. Trinita on Via Tornabuoni
   Open daily 8:00-12:00, 16:00-18:00
   Sun 16:00-18:00

5. A *bottega* was a group of artists who worked together in a collaborative "workshop" atmosphere to complete a project. The workers were hired by the artist, and the work of art was considered to be the work of the artist who would sign the project himself.

6. Luca della Robbia's marble *Cantoria* may be seen in the museum **Opera del Duomo.**
   Della Robbia's ceramic *Resurrection* is in the Duomo over the doorway of the N Sacristy.
   To this day the secret of the della Robbia process for ceramics and glaze is unknown.

   Opera del Duomo, temporarily closed for restoration in 2014 *(Check if restoration is completed)*
   Piazza del Duomo 9
   Open Mon-Sat 9:00-19:30 Sun 9:00-13:40

7. Wax models of the Black Plague, created in the 17th century by Gaetano Giulio Zumbo (1656-1701) are in **La Specola.** The museum was part of the Boboli Gardens and was originally the observatory of the Medici. Zumbo modeled in colored wax. For the Grand Duke he created a series of six models depicting the progressive "Corruption after Death:" a dying man, a corpse, a corpse starting to decompose, half decomposed, completely decomposed, eaten by worms. These are on display in the museum.
   La Specola   Via Romana 17
   Open weekdays 9:00-13:00
   Closed Wed
   Sat 9:00-17:00, Sun 9:00-13:00

8. The *Misericordia* is on Piazza del Duomo, the SW corner of Via Calzauioli beside the campanile. "The brotherhood receives men and women of every social rank who wish to help with moral and material aid." All service is anonymous. Goals have not changed in the course of ages. "Misericordia is considered the most prestigious, most esteemed and loved Florentine institution, the most ancient one in the world with a continuous activity for more than 760 years."
   Misericordia   Piazza del Duomo
   Open Mon 9:00-12:30 and 3:00-5:00

9 The *Bigallo* is on the corner of Piazza del Duomo and Via Calzauioli.
   Tourist Office   **Bigallo Museum**
   Open Mon-Sat 10:30-4:30   Open on the half hour with a reservation at the door
   Sun and Holidays 9:30-12:30

10. The rood screen in **Santa Maria Novella** ran along the edge where the steps in the nave now lead up to the bench seating. All the area where the benches are now was the sacred space behind the rood screen, accessible only to the clergy, choir, and nobles. The *Trinity* was located midway in what was then the public space of the nave, beside a font of Holy Water which no longer exists.
    Santa Maria Novella   Piazza Santa Maria Novella
    Open Mon-Thurs 9:00-17:30
    Fri 11:00-17:30
    Sat 9:00-17:00
    Sun 13:00-17:00

11. *Stemma* is a family crest or coat-of-arms.

Chapter Three

In The Footsteps Of Michelangelo

"Simone da Fiesole had started to carve a giant figure . . . and left the block completely botched and misshapen . . . the cathedral wardens decided that they would let Michelangelo have the marble, as being of something of little value, and telling themselves that since the stone was of no use . . . either botched or broken up, whatever Michelangelo made would be worthwhile."

"Anyone who has ever seen Michelangelo's David *has no need to see anything else by any other sculptor, living or dead."*

> — Giorgio Vasari
> 1568 *Lives of the Artists*

Since 1434, the Medici family had spent 663,000 florins (today c.460 million USD) for charity, buildings and taxes. "I do not regret this for though many would consider it better to have a part of that sum in their purse, I consider it to have been a great honour to our state, and I think the money was well-expended and I am well-pleased."

> — Lorenzo The Magnificent
> 1471 "Letter to his friends"

16 August 1501

"I got the contract, I got the contract!" Michelangelo was so excited he startled all the lions in the cages behind Palazzo della Signoria[1] as he ran down Via dei Leoni on the way to his friend Granacci's house. Since he had first seen the huge piece of marble as a boy in the yard of the workshop of the Opera del Duomo[2] behind the Cathedral, Michelangelo had dreamed of his chisel sinking into *il gigante*, the carrara marble block almost ruined forty years ago by other sculptors. Now even Leonardo da Vinci had refused the block, and the commission for the *David* was his!

Michelangelo was thirteen years old when he and Granacci were apprenticed to Ghirlandaio to learn the craft of fresco painting. Michelangelo did not really want to learn painting, he had grown up among stone cutters and he wanted to sculpt! When Michelangelo was very young, his mother was often ill and his father sent him to the town of Settignano where the Buonarroti family owned a marble quarry[3] and a small farm. Living there for the first years of his life Michelangelo learned by osmosis all he knew about stone and how to cut it. He often told Granacci "I sucked in the hammer and chisels I use for my statues from my wet-nurse's milk."[4]

The Easter when Michelangelo was three, Francesco de' Pazzi murdered Giuliano de' Medici in the Cathedral. Michelangelo was in Settignano, and his mother was pregnant with her third son. Father later told Michelangelo that he was glad that his son had not been in Florence to witness the horror. He would remember forever the sight of bodies hanging from the windows of Palazzo della Signoria and hacked arms and legs thrown down into the Piazza. Michelangelo's mother survived the uproar of that day, but was never well again after two more sons were born. She died when Michelangelo was six, having birthed five boys in nine years.

As an apprentice of thirteen to Ghirlandaio in the Santa Maria Novella commission, Michelangelo always made certain to leave home early on his way to work so he could walk the extra blocks to pass by the Opera del Duomo work yard in back of the Cathedral to see what was new.[5] The Buonarroti clan rented a house in the Santa Croce district near a circular street which in ancient times used to be the Roman amphitheatre at Via dell' Anguilara, Via Bentaccordi and Via Torta.[6] The tiers of seats in the old Roman colosseum had made an easy solution to the housing problem in Florence when the city began to grow after the Black Plague, and it had expanded out into the suburbs. Even the Church of Santa Croce was losing its vineyards and olive trees.

The work shop of the great sculptor Donatello was in the yard of the Opera del Duomo behind the Cathedral. Donatello's work could be seen everywhere in Piazza del Duomo, from the Cathedral to the Baptistery to the Campanile. Donatello had been dead barely twenty years, and for Michelangelo and other Florentines, he was the greatest sculptor who ever lived. His statues were so real that they seemed to talk. Everyone in Florence old enough to remember Donatello knows the story of how he told the Campanile statue, "pumpkin-headed" *Lo Zuccone*, "Speak, damn you, speak!"

Donatello lived in a house next door[7] to the Cathedral work yard and anyone walking down the street as the name changes from Via dei Leoni to Via del Proconsolo can see it. Michelangelo dreamed of adding his name to the list of the three *Davids* in Florence: Donatello's marble *David*, Donatello's bronze *David* in the Medici Palace, and Verocchio's bronze *David*.

The Buonarroti family was as old as the Medici, Strozzi, and Tornabuoni. They had paid taxes in Florence for thirty centuries. The family was in a slack period now, but Uncle Lodovico was certain that times would change with such an intelligent and gifted nephew as Michelangelo – if only he would give up the idea of this art business. Lodovico was proud of his ancestry and worried that an artist in the family would bring disgrace.

But disgrace was not to be Michelangelo's destiny. After only a few months of working at fresco with Ghirlandaio, Lorenzo the Magnificent asked Ghirlandaio to recommend his most promising students to come to work in the Medici Sculpture Garden. At the age of fourteen, Michelangelo Buonarroti and his friend Francesco Granacci went to the court of Lorenzo the Magnificent to live and study at Palazzo Medici. The boys had free access to the gardens under the supervision of Bertoldo, a former pupil of Donatello. Bertoldo was keeper of Lorenzo's ancient Roman sculptures

The Sculpture Garden in the Medici Palace

The reading room of the Laurentian Library designed by Michelangelo. He designed the reading desks, each desk row has a sign on the edge which tells what books are available to be read on that desk row.

and a noted sculptor himself. He was too old to work, his job was to teach promising young sculptors and oversee the restoration of antiques.

In the Medici palace, the boys lived among the social elite of Florence: poets, scholars, humanists, philosophers, politicians. By the age of sixteen Michelangelo had spent two happy years in the Medici household and had created two marble reliefs, the *Madonna of the Stairs* and the *Battle of the Centaurs*.[8] "Centaurs" was a commission from Lorenzo himself depicting a story from Greek mythology with half-men, half-horse creatures fighting a battle using stones as weapons. The relief was an amazing work for a sixteen-year-old who had only seen men and horses in battle on Roman sarcophagi, fully dressed with armor, sword and shield.

There was no lack of art for Michelangelo to study in Florence. He could sketch from ancient Greek and Roman sculpture in the Medici Palace, from revered Giotto frescos in the Bardi Chapel at the church of Santa Croce, and from forward-looking Masaccio frescoes across the river in the Carmine.[9] He was even invited to see the newest art works in the Medici villa of Castello, Botticelli's huge *Birth of Venus* and *Spring*. Some artists were commissioned to create stage scenery and dinner decorations, and others even designed for parades.

There was one *Carnavale*[10] that Michelangelo never would forget. He first heard the sound of the trumpets and drums along the river and by the time the parade made the turn from Via Tornabuoni toward the Cathedral, it was followed by half of Florence. Word had spread of Piero di Cosimo's[11] float "The Triumph of Death" on a large cart escorted by bony, cadaverous horses mounted by costumed figures of death. Michelangelo had to chase the parade almost all the way to Piazza Signoria before he could catch up enough to get a good look at the cart. It was hauled by black buffaloes with white-painted faces and was topped by an immense figure of Death holding a scythe. Every time the trumpets played, the cart would stop and tombs around the edge would open. Eerie chanting masked men would emerge in black robes painted to look like skeletons.[12]

After Lorenzo died in 1492, things were never the same for Michelangelo or for Florence. Twenty-year-old Piero de' Medici succeeded his father as ruler of Florence; Piero was friendly to Michelangelo, but had little interest in art. Michelangelo was soon back home living with his father and brothers. An out-of-work nineteen-year-old, Michelangelo cast around for what to do next.

As a young boy, Michelangelo had observed and sketched the bodies of the lightly clothed stonecutters working in the heat of the Tuscan summer. What if he could dissect human bodies and really see anatomy from the inside out? He knew the prior of Santo Spirito, an out-of-the-way church across the river which had a hospital for the indigent where the dead were kept before burial. But to cut open the human body was strictly forbidden in the Catholic Church. Would the prior be open-minded, and would he be impressed by the request of a young man so gifted that he was coming from the patronage of Lorenzo the Magnificent?

Michelangelo was allowed to dissect in Santo Spirito for two years, studying and sketching anatomy. He repaid the prior by sculpting a wooden crucifix for the church of Santo Spirito. This was to be an unusual representation of a dying Christ with a delicate "heavenly" body on the cross, a conception of a nineteen-year-old confronting the reality of death for the first time.[13]

The year 1494 was a momentous year; a heavy snow fell in Florence in January and the plague returned. Ghirlandaio, Michelangelo's mentor of his youth, died of the plague that January at the age of forty-five. Not a very promising start to the year that Michelangelo turned nineteen. The political situation was precarious with Piero's short rule of two years. Michelangelo's feeling of being unappreciated was confirmed when Piero "commissioned" him to make a snowman in the courtyard of Palazzo Medici with the January snow. Michelangelo was starting to see the writing on the wall, and was beginning to think it was time to search elsewhere for appreciative patrons.

Under Piero's haphazard reign, political Florence became increasingly unstable and blood and thunder preachers

FAR LEFT PHOTO BY: Maggie Suckow

PHOTO BY: Rona Commins

(above) A model of the cart which was used to move the David. The model is housed in Casa Buonarroti.

(left) Michelangelo's David was in this location in front of Palazzo della Signoria until it was moved to the Accademia in 1882

PHOTO BY: Rona Commins

The inner courtyard of the Medici Palace where the teen-aged Michelangelo lived with Lorenzo the Magnificent. The Medici stemma or coat-of-arms is displayed as part of the frieze decoration above the arches.

found wide audiences. Savonarola , a charismatic Dominican based at the church of San Marco,[14] had a particularly disturbing influence, denouncing the corruption of Florence and prophesying the imminent doom of the sinful city. The invasion of Italy by Charles VIII of France added fuel to the unrest. Art could not be rewarded in a city where a preacher like Savonarola could cause even an artist such as Botticelli to throw his work on a bonfire in Piazza della Signoria.[15]

Michelangelo left Florence and worked in Bologna then Rome. At the age of twenty-three he created the startlingly beautiful Rome *Pieta*, Mary holding her dead son on her lap, and was heralded as Italy's foremost sculptor. Back in Florence *sans* Medici, the new Republic wished to commission an artist for the giant block of carrara marble which had been lying unfinished in the work yard behind the Duomo for forty years. When word reached Michelangelo in Rome, he knew that this was *il gigante*, the stone he had dreamed to use as his own David! Wanting this lucrative and challenging commission, Michelangelo returned to Florence as fast as possible and won the *Arte della Lana*[16] Wool Guild contract for a seventeen-foot-tall statue:

16 Aug 1501

> *The Consuls of the Arte della Lana and the Lords Overseers . . . have chosen . . . the worthy Master, Michelangelo, the son of Lodovico Buonarroti, a citizen of Florence, to the end that he may make, and finish, and bring to perfection the male figure known as the Giant, nine braccia in height, already blocked in marble by Maestro Agostino, of Florence, and badly blocked; now stored in the workshops of the Cathedral.*

> *The work shall be completed within the period and term of two years next ensuing . . . with a salary and payment . . . of six broad florins of gold for every month . . . When the said work and the said male figure of marble shall be finished, then the Consuls and the Overseers who shall at that time be in authority shall judge whether it merits a higher reward, being guided therein by the dictates of their own consciences.*[17]

The *David* was originally envisioned by the Opera del Duomo committee to be one of a series of statues of Old Testament prophets which would be placed on the roofline at the east end of the Duomo atop the buttresses. When Michelangelo's statue was completed, the Opera could see that the six-ton *David* was in no way going to be lifted up to the roof top. Besides, it was too beautiful to be placed so high out of sight.

A committee of thirty artists and citizens including three gold smiths, a jeweler, an embroiderer, a fife player, a woodcarver, a carpenter and the Herald of the Palace were summoned "to give and lay down their opinion etc. and to indicate the place where the statue should be installed."[18] Michelangelo had his opinion, but among the thirty on the committee nine different positions were proposed.

There seemed to be intrigue involved in the final decision. While some opted for a very visible location on the steps of the Cathedral or in front of Palazzo della Signoria others, maybe for reasons of professional jealousy, chose a more hidden location in the back of Loggia dei Lanzi. Botticelli magnanimously recommended a place beside the Cathedral with a newly created pedestal. Artists Leonardo da Vinci, Giulio da Sangallo, and Piero di Cosimo (of the *Carnavale* float) pointed out faults and made the back-of-the-Loggia recommendation. Notes taken at the meeting quote Piero di Cosimo.

> *"in view of the imperfection of the marble which is soft and spoiled by having remained in the open, I do not think it could last . . . because if it is put in the open it will soon be destroyed, and it has to be covered."*[19]

In June of 1504 when David was moved to Palazzo della Signoria it took four days to roll it on round logs the half mile from the work yard in back of the Duomo to the Piazza. The David remained outside in the weather on the steps of Palazzo della Signoria for three-hundred eighty years. It was the first time since antiquity that a large nude statue was exhibited in a public place. It was only allowed because it was by Michelangelo and because it was a community symbol of the defense of civil liberty against the rival city-states and against the Medici who were now out of power. Medici power had been exhibited in this very Piazza, and more was yet to come.

A poem written by Michelangelo in a letter to a friend complaining of the difficulty of painting the Sistine chapel ceiling: Elizabeth Hall, *The Sonnets of Michelangelo Buonarroti*, p. 89

Poem to Giovanni da Pistoia

I've got myself a goiter from this strain

As water gives the cats in Lombardy

Or maybe it is in some other country;

My belly's pushed by force beneath my chin

My beard toward Heaven, I feel the back of my brain

Upon my neck, I grow the breast of a Harpy;

My brush, above my face continually,

Makes it a splendid floor by dripping down.

My loins have penetrated to my pauch,

My rump's a crupper, as a counterweight,

And pointless the unseeing steps I go.

In front of me my skin is being stretched

While it folds up behind and forms a knot,

And I am bending like a Syrian bow.

And judgment, hence, must grow,

Borne in the mind, pecular and untrue;

You cannot shoot well when the gun's askew.

John, [Giovanni] come to the rescue

Of my dead painting now, and of my honor;

I'm not in a good place, and I'm no painter.

1. Lions were a symbol of Florence. The first recorded lion cage in Florence was near the Baptistry in the 12th century. Cages were eventually placed in Via dei Leoni in back of Palazzo della Signoria as a symbol of the power of the Florentine Republic. During the Renaissance in 15th century Florence there were as many as 28 lions caged behind the Palazzo.

   There is a surviving shopping list that includes the cost of lion feed: in 1336, food for the city's lions (along with torches and candles) came to 2400 lire. By means of comparison, the city's musicians and heralds, including trumpeters, drummers, shawm players, and ten herald trumpet players, cost the city 1000 lire for that year. The lions ate well. Elizabeth Holt, **The Documentary History of Art.**

2. The **Opera del Duomo** was the name given to the board of directors of the Cathedral works, as well as the workshops and other establishments attached to these constructions.

3. These were vague **communal property rights** like the American open range before barbed wire and railroad grants sectioned it off. No one owned a deed to a quarry.

4. Vasari, *Lives of the Artists.*

5. The Opera del Duomo work shop for the Cathedral, where Michelangelo carved the David, is still in the same location in back of the cathedral, but it is now a museum.

   Museo dell'Opera del Duomo *Temporarily closed for restoration 2014.* ....Piazza Duomo 9
   Open Mon-Sat 9:00-19:30
   Sun 9:00-13:40.

6. Irving Stone, *Agony and the Ecstacy.*

7. Donatello's home is now a cafe beside Museo dell'Opera del Duomo. Above the café and the entrance to the home there is a marble bust of Donatello.

8. These two early relief sculptures, *Madonna of the Stairs* and *Battle of the Centaurs*, are in Michelangelo's home, now a museum. In 1508 when he was thirty-three years old, Michelangelo bought a house on Via Ghibellina in Florence. His heir and grand-nephew, Michelangelo the Younger, enlarged the house and made it into a "shrine" museum.

   Casa Buonarroti ....Via Ghibellina 70
   Open daily 9:30-16:00 (Closed Tues.)

9. Giotto and Masaccio were early Renaissance artists who were the first to depict expression and individuality on the faces of people in fresco. Anyone intending to be an artist would go to Santa Croce and the Carmine to sketch and study.

10. Carnival is a holiday 40 days before Easter with a parade of floats, horseback riders, bands, dancers, etc. The *Carnavale* described here actually occurred in 1507.

11. Piero di Cosimo (1462-1522) was a Florentine painter, son of a goldsmith. He was pyrophobic and did not cook his food. He ate only eggs which he boiled 50 at a time while boiling glue for his artwork.

    Piero di Cosimo lived in the time of Savonarola and had an affinity for the bizarre. Vasari op. cit.

12. Vasari op. cit.

13. Michelangelo's **wood crucifix** (authenticity disputed) may be seen at the church of Santo Spirito.

    Santo Spirito ....Piazza Santo Spirito
    Open daily 9:30-12:30 and 16:00-18:00 (Closed Wed)

14. **San Marco Monastery and Museum** ....Piazza San Marco 1
    Open 8:15-13:50, Sat & Sun to 16:50 (Closed Mon)

15. The location of the burning of the preacher Savonarola and his "Bonfire of the Vanities" is marked with a circular plaque in Piazza della Signoria in front of the Neptune Fountain to the left of Palazzo Vecchio.

16. The *Arte della Lana* was the very rich wool guild, one of the great Florence corporations.

    It was responsible for the upkeep and decoration of the cathedral. The Consuls were the *Arte della Lana's* elected leaders.

17. The contract for the David is cited in the Journal of Luca Landucci (1450-1519), a dealer in *speziale*, spices and drugs.

18. Elizabeth Holt, op. cit.

19. The sculpture of David sat outside in the weather in Piazza della Signoria until it was moved to the Accademia in 1882. The Accademia di Belle Arti was founded in 1563, connected to it is the Academy of Music *Conservatorio di Luigi Cherubini* founded in 1784. Both were in existence when the Tribune was purpose-built in 1882 to house the David. In 1910 a David replica was placed in front of Palazzo Vecchio.
    Accademia di Belle Arti ....Via Ricasoli 66
    Open daily 8:15-8:50 (Closed Mon)

Chapter Four

Medici Revenge

"Lorenzo was a man endowed by nature, training, and practice with such enormous ingenuity . . . he had so able and versatile a mind that whatever he turned to in his pursuits as a boy, he learned and possessed perfectly . . . he learned to dance, fire arrows, sing, ride, join in games, play diverse musical instruments . . . and I believe that being inspired by the magnitude of his ability, when he found our citizens timid and of a servile spirit . . . he resolved to transfer to himself all public dignity, power, and authority and in the end, like Julius Caesar, to make himself lord of the republic."

— Alamanno Rinuccini
1475 *Ricordi*

Captain at Arms to Count Girolamo Riario: "O My Lord, one hangs thieves and traitors, and I am not that sort. I deserve to die sword in hand, like any other brave man at arms."

— Quoted in Lauro Martines
The Lords of Romagna

"The conspirators were rounded up one by one and brought back dead or alive, whole or in bits."

— Barbara Hodgson
Italy Out of hand

14 April 1488

"Assassination was the same in Forli as in Florence – by poison, strangulation, or the steel blade."[1] In 1488 Forli was still struggling from the effects of the plague with a population of 8000-9000. Fifty miles south-west, with only mountains to intervene, energetic Florence had already grown to a post-plague population of five times that many.

For ten years, Count Girolamo Riario, Lord of Forli and Imola, had to be very careful. He was one of the chief conspirators in the assassination attempt on the two Medici brothers in Florence Cathedral in April of 1478. Fifty miles and ten years were not much of a separation between him and Lorenzo de' Medici. The Count had outwitted three assassination attempts on his life but Lorenzo was forever intriguing against him, sowing discord among his workers and soldiers who were jealous because his uncle, Pope Sixtus, had given him the lucrative fiefs of Forli and Imola. In April 1488, ten years after the 26 April assassination attempt in the Cathedral of Florence, Count Girolamo Riario was the only one of the conspirators still left alive.

On that bloody Sunday morning when Giuliano de' Medici was assassinated, retaliation was immediate and brutal. The Lord Prior government officials called in "the Eight" who were responsible for prosecuting political crime. They suspended statutes and extended emergency powers to seize control of the rebelling soldiers and leaders who had marched to Palazzo della Signoria expecting to head a citizen revolt against the Medici. But they were taken by surprise: there was no citizen revolt. By evening every one of the mutineers was ensnared in the Government Palace.

It was a time for peaceable Florentines to stay in their homes. In Piazza della Signoria, anyone arrested was summarily hung from the high windows of the Palace or thrown down to the milling throngs in the square. Even the nine-year-old Machiavelli did not want to be outdoors when bodies were being stripped naked and

Palazzo Vecchio (Palazzo della Signoria), the government palace where Pazzi and other conspirators were hung from the windows after the assassination of Giuliano de' Medici.

hacked apart by a furious crowd. Later that evening a torch-lit procession chanting *"Palle!, Palle!"*[2] in support of the Medici, dragged dismembered body parts through the streets, waving heads and arms aloft on the points of bloodied spears.

Machiavelli was on the other side of town when he saw men dragging a pair of legs past the Cathedral to the front doors of Lorenzo's Medici Palace. One man was carrying a head on the point of a lance, and another had "an arm, borne aloft on a spit." Machiavelli recorded that over the next four days, there were "so many deaths that the streets were filled with parts of men."[3]

The lions in Via dei Leoni were roaring at the smell of blood by the time the two priests who had made the attempt on Lorenzo's life were dragged to Piazza della Signoria. The beaten and mutilated priests, minus ears and noses, were turned over to the Priors and the Eight to be hanged from the front windows of the government palace, Palazzo della Signoria. The Count of Montesecco was spared the indignities of the crowd. He made his confession at the Bargello,[4] the criminal-court building, where he was

given the "gentleman's death" of decapitation without disfiguration in front of the double doors of the courtyard. On 21 July, the Eight issued an order to pay Botticelli forty large gold florins "for his work in painting the traitors"[5] on the exterior walls of the Bargello.

The next day after the death of Giuliano was not "business as usual," and in fact shops were shut down. Reprisals continued and Count Montesecco's men were arrested, even though he had refused to shed blood the day before in the Cathedral. Eight of his foot soldiers and several of his knights were hung from Palazzo della Signoria windows. In the afternoon after the nooses were cut, the bodies fell down into the piazza where the temporarily satiated Florentines allowed them to remain all night. The lions caged in back of the Palazzo kept up a continual din that night, clamoring for their share of the spoils. The next morning, an eye-witness recorded, '"The bodies were fitted into the casements of the shops of notaries at the palace of the Podestá, [the Bargello] and there, bare

The lion of Florence, the Marzocco, a marble sculpture in Palazzo Vecchio.

skin and upright, they were left to lean, so they looked like men depicted or portrayed to look alive, because they were as stiff and naked as the day they were born."[6]

Since the death of their father nine years previously, Lorenzo and Giuliano had been co-rulers of the state. From a young age, Lorenzo was the son who had been groomed by his father Piero, and grandfather Cosimo, to take over the leadership of the family. Even at the early age of five-and-a-half, Lorenzo's grandfather had sent him on a state visit to Naples all dressed up in the French manner and accompanied by a splendid retinue. In many ways Lorenzo was the opposite of his younger brother, Giuliano. Lorenzo's was a "patron of the arts" image, Giuliano's was a favorite, handsome "golden boy" of Florence image.

An excellent horseman, Giuliano had taken part in many tournaments, wearing the colors of first one lady, then another. Lorenzo, by contrast, was an artist who wrote poetry in his native Tuscan. In his poetry he celebrated life, expressing also the fragility and instability of the human condition which he saw everywhere around him. A lover of learning, Lorenzo's father Cosimo had started the collection of books which became the Medici Library. Lorenzo's agents retrieved large numbers of classical works from the East, and he employed a large workshop to copy his books and disseminate their contents across Europe.[7]

Lorenzo had a heavy face, large flat nose and swarthy complexion and was not considerd a handsome man.[8] His charm lay in his manner and his tall and robust physique which gave him an impression of dignity. Whether portrayed as a young man in the chapel of Medici Palazzo *Procession of the Magi*,[9] as a benign head-of-state in the summer apartments of Palazzo Pitti,[10] or a middle-aged political ruler in the Sassetti Chapel of Santa Trinita,[11] his nose and complexion were unmistakable.

After the assassination, Lorenzo became sole head of state; he alone was responsible to uphold the traditional family duty of defending family honor and wreaking family revenge. During the next four days, all Pazzi brothers and cousins were hunted and arrested. They were accused of having connived in the plot, but no proof was found. Their crime was that they had committed the treason of holding their tongues. All Pazzi were disenfranchised, disinherited, and if not killed, exiled. All vestiges of their existence in Florence were erased. Family crests were hacked off buildings: the Pazzi coat-of-arms with two vertical dolphins back to back was never again to be seen in Florence.

The Pazzi name was expunged from city roles, their properties and goods were confiscated. City Priors and the Eight held investigations to uncover the complete wealth of the Pazzi. All Florentine business ledgers were subject to government seizure: lists of debtors, Pazzi partners in trade and banking, all properties, farms and buildings, records of credits and investments in Florentine government debt.

Pazzi property must be liquidated. Pazzi horses and mules were the first things to go, sold at an auction before the government had to spend too much money on their feed. The biggest sale of all occurred on the first day of June and was advertised to all of Tuscany: a huge yard sale, so large it was to be held in the *Zecca*, the Florence mint.

PHOTO BY: Rona Commins

These two archways which were originally windows in Palazzo della Signoria (Palazzo Vecchio) were opened up to be used as a studiolo for Machiavelli when he was employed by the Medici family.

PHOTO BY: Rona Commins

In front of the Neptune Fountain ("Big Whitey") is the circular plaque which marks the spot on the pavement of Piazza della Signoria where Savonarola was burned at the stake. This is the same location where Savonarola lit his "Bonfire of the Vanities", burning Florentine jewels, clothing, make-up, hair-pieces, fabrics, books, and many priceless works of art.

All Pazzi possessions, household goods, clothing, furniture, linens, pictures, etc., were up for the highest bidder. There was such a massive array of items that reports recorded that it filled the *Zecca* "from one side to the other." People with carts and horses were seen for hours hauling loads of goods out through the city gates, especially through *Porta Romana*[12] which led to the wealthy villas of the countryside.

The boys of Florence found some excitement of their own when they heard a chorus of dogs barking outside the city walls. Running as fast as they could they followed the happy yaps through the gate of *Porte Sante*[13] to the burial ground for the unsanctified. The freshly dug grave of the father of the Pazzi clan was under attack by marauding dogs; what better attraction to a city could there be than the smell of days of bloodshed. It was not easy to convince the dogs to leave their prey to a pack of boys. With dogs running around helter-skelter, the boys dug up the corpse of Francesco de' Pazzi and found the rope still hanging around his neck. Pulling it by the noose, they dragged it back into the city, beating it with sticks like a dog.

It was a three-week-old stinking body that dripped on the stones of Piazza della Signoria as it was dragged around the corner to the Pazzi Palace. The boys banged Jacopo's head against his own door and said: "Who's in there? Who's inside? What, is there no one here to receive the master and his entourage?"[14] Then they dumped Jacopo's body off the Ponte alle Grazie bridge into the Arno river. A few days later other boys downstream pulled it from the water, hung it on a willow tree, and beat it as though they were beating a carpet. They threw it back into the Arno where it floated down the river under the bridges of Pisa and out to sea.

The Pazzi brothers and cousins were imprisoned for life in the tower of Volterra. In April 1482, the sentence was commuted and changed to perpetual exile outside Italy. The Pazzi name and coat of arms were outlawed in Florence, including their association with the "holy-fire" cart and celebration at Easter. Lorenzo ordered a life-sized wax statue to be made of himself to be installed in the church of Santissima Annunziation[15] as a votive thank-offering for his escape from the Easter assassins.

14 April 1488, exactly ten years after the Easter assassination, Riario was slashed to death in the government palace of Forli. His naked corpse was thrown into the central square, gaped at and violated by angry citizens. He may have been Count Girolamo Riario, Lord of Forli and Imola, nephew of the late Pope Sixtus IV, but there was no escape: "The taste for vengeance was a virile duty in Renaissance Florence."[16]

For ten years Count Riario's greatest expense had been for a body of guardsmen and an extra company of one hundred soldiers to protect himself from Lorenzo. No matter, two brothers of the Orsi family, his fiscal agents, had a disagreement; there were heated quarrels about money. As local noblemen, the two Orsi brothers enjoyed the "privilege of the gilded key," they had a right to call on Count Riario without invitation. They went to the palace after dinner on Monday, 14 April 1488. One diverted the few servants in the dining room as the other brother greeted Riario with the thrust of a short sword. Riario attempted to scurry under the table to protect himself; he was left alone as the terrorized attendants fled; the noblemen slit the Count's throat with a steel blade. Later they wrote to Lorenzo, "we have wreaked revenge for you."[17]

Renaissance Italy's supreme triad – Family, Politics, Money – had triumphed.

Would it carry into another generation with Cosimo I and the beautiful Eleonora di Toledo?

1. Martines p.226.
2. *"Palle"* are the balls of the Medici crest. The people who chanted *Palle* were in favor of the Medici remaining in power.
3. Machiavelli, *Florentine Histories*.
4. The Bargello was the criminal-court building in Renaissance Florence.
   National Sculpture Museum of the Bargello ....Via del Proconsolo 4
   Open daily 8:15-18:00 (Closed Mon)
5. Quoted in Martines, p.135.
6. Martines p. 129, from Poliziano, *Congiura*.
7. The Laurentian Library was designed by Michelangelo in 1524 to house the Medici collection of books. The long reading room contains desks designed by Michelangelo. The entry staircase was copied many times by other architects. See photos pp. 32 and 67.

   Biblioteca Medicea Laurenziana ....Inside the cloister of San Lorenzo church
   Open Mon-Sat 9:00-13:00 (Closed Sun)

   Church of San Lorenzo ....Piazza San Lorenzo
   Open Mon-Sat 10:00-17:00 • Sun 13:30-17:00
8. A cast of Lorenzo's face at his death is in **Museo degli Argenti** at **Palazzo Pitti**.
   Museo degli Argenti
   Open daily 8:15-18:30, and to 19:30 June-August. ....Closed first and last Mondays of the month.
   Cumulative ticket #2 includes Boboli Gardens, Costume Gallery, and Porcelain Museum
9. Gozzoli's *Procession of the Magi* is in the private Medici chapel
   Palazzo Medici-Ricardi...Via Cavour 3
   Open daily 9:00-19:00 (Closed Wed)
10. The fresco of Lorenzo the Magnificent is in the second room, on the lower floor of Palazzo Pitti.
    Museo degli Argenti
    Open daily 8:15-18:30, and to 19:30 June-August. ....(Closed first and last Mondays of the month)
    Cumulative ticket #2 includes Boboli Gardens, Costume Gallery, and Porcelain Museum
11. **Sassetti Chapel** is in the church of **Santa Trinita**.
    Santa Trinita ....Piazza S. Trinita on Via Tornabuoni
    Open daily 8:00-12:00, 16:00-18:00
    Sun 16:00-18:00.
12. **Porta Romana** was the city gate on the road leading to Rome and Siena. It may be seen at the south end of Via Romana. The gate was built in 1326 and is the largest and best-preserved of the seven remaining gates of Florence. It contains its original doors, locks, and is surmounted by a marble Medici coat-of-arms. It is possible to walk on the wall, there is parking near-by.
13. *Wikipedia* Florence.
14. Martines p.131. **The Ponte alle Grazie** was at that time called the Ponte Rubaconte. It is one bridge up-river (E) from Ponte Vecchio.
15. **Santissima Annunziata** ....Piazza SS Anunnziata, N end of Via dei Servi
    Open 16:00-17:50
16. Martines, p.7.
17. Martines p.9.

Chapter Five

For Love Of A Spanish Princess

"My dearest daughter, much do I pray thee and even command thee, that thou distress not thyself because I have given thee in marriage . . . Now must thou leave the dominion of thy father and go unto that of thy husband and thy lord . . . Hearken unto my counsels, and receive them as though they were commandments . . . The seventh commandment is, that thou shalt not do any great thing of thine own accord without the consent of thine husband, however good reason there may seem unto thee for doing it. And take heed that thou dost on no account say unto him, 'my advice was better than thine' . . ."

— A Mother's Farewell
1350 *Avvertimenti di Maritaggio*

"You wives, when you have married into a house of two or three brothers, be careful not to cause divisions between the brothers or to envy your sister-in-law every time she has a child and you do not, or she has a boy and you a girl, or hers is nice looking and yours is ugly."

— San Bernardino of Siena
1420 *Prediche volgari*

"There is no dowry, no matter how big, that is not all worn on the bride's back when she leaves to go to her husband."

— Alessandra Strozzi
1465 *Lettere*

25 June 1539

Today we arrived at Poggio a Caiano, what a beautiful villa! How lovely Tuscany is in June with the red poppies punctuating the yellow sunflower fields. After sailing eleven days from Naples, Livorno felt steady under my feet, and unloading seven galleys full of Spanish nobility, servants, clothes, and jewels didn't seem such a daunting task. My brother hired carriages, the porters packed everything in, and we were off to see the Leaning Tower!

Father had seemed worried when we left him in Naples for this journey. Seven years ago when I was ten years old and our family had just arrived in Italy, it had only been three years since the plague had reappeared here. It was quite a responsibility for father to be called by Charles V to take his family, leave Spain, and go to Italy as viceroy 'Don Pedro Alvarez de Toledo' to rule Naples the largest city in the Spanish Empire.

Here on the road to Pisa, imagine my surprise when Cosimo appeared riding to meet me like a glorious phantom; tradition says the bridegroom is supposed to greet his bride at the gates of the city. He was days ahead of time, so excited he could not wait any longer! Cosimo with all his friends, horses, dogs, and baggage rode beside my carriage and our whole noisy entourage tumbled into the Campo Santo to see the Leaning Tower. They call the Cathedral 'Duomo' here. If Pisa is this beautiful, what will Florence be like?

On the second day my love-sick nineteen-year-old bridegroom surprised me again. I was wearing my best color, "a gown of purplish violet velvet embroidered with gold" with a "gold coif" on my head.[1] Cosimo put the most beautiful golden chain around my neck and placed a gold ring set with a diamond on my finger. We had actually been married by proxy three months ago in Naples, so all this was now formality, but what a lovely surprise! When Cosimo asked for my hand, my father almost didn't allow the marriage because he wanted my older sister to marry first. Luckily Cosimo refused, even though he received less money as a dowry for me than he would have received if he had married my older sister.

At the Medici Villa of Poggia a Caiano,[2] we have four whole days to dally and spend our time as we choose before we must travel to appear in regal retinue at the gates of the city of Florence. We are due to arrive there on the twenty-ninth, processing together through the Porta al Prato down Via Larga to the Palace of the Medici family. I will be seventeen years old.

This villa at Poggio a Caiana, called "The Villa on the Hill" by the Medici family, has the most interesting buildings I have ever seen. Cosimo says it was one of the first built in the latest Italian style by Giuliano da Sangallo. It has rooms arranged around a big central courtyard like the Roman ones I saw with my father in Pompeii. The entrance is on the *primo piano*[3] instead of on the *terra* as any other house I have seen here in Italy. There are six columns at the front door on *primo piano*, and that makes the entrance doors appear to be floating in the air. A blue and white terracotta frieze above the doors and columns completes the picture with the punctuaton mark of a pointed roof. It feels like we are living like free spirit-nymphs, open to the outdoors – I hope we will see this place again after our wedding!

Our church wedding in Florence took place on 29 June 1539 in San Lorenzo, which is the church just behind the Medici Palace.[4] All we had to do was cross through the piazza to get there. San Lorenzo is the parish church of the Medici family, but nobody has to tell you that, you can see it with your own eyes. The ceiling is flat, which is unusual, and the whole ceiling from end to end is decorated with gilded Medici crests.[5] Cosimo told me that our wedding would be the last festivities to take place in the Medici Palazzo on Via Larga, we will soon be moving to a bigger, more prestigious place!

Since it was summer, it was decided that our banquet and the theatrical performance for our wedding would be open-air. The Medici Palace has two courtyards, and we would be in the second courtyard which is the garden.

"The space of the courtyard-garden was transformed into a closed room by an awning of sky blue cloth, drawn across to form a sort of ceiling; hanging from this were cupids with bows and arrows and a lighted lamp. The stage was situated on the north side of the rectangular enclosure of the courtyard; the lady spectators were accommodated on tiered stands of seats on the long sides while the prince and his court occupied a pavilion set up in the loggia at the rear of the south side."[6]

During the wedding banquet there was a parade of forty-eight allegorical figures representing the lands, mountains and rivers of Tuscany. Each figure sang a song in homage to Cosimo de' Medici and his consort Eleonora di Toledo. Apollo opened and closed the procession by playing 'divinely' upon his lyre. After Apollo left, the stage was empty and Aurora appeared high above sitting on a flowered red cloth. She was blonde with wings tinged in white and red, dressed in a gown with gold and silver stripes, with sandals made of interlaced flowers. Aurora was singing and combing her hair with an ivory comb.[7]

Then we had a second spettacolo[8] for our wedding! I think it was chosen especially in honor of where Cosimo and I spent our first night together, in Pisa. The play *Il Commodo* had back drops and stage machinery designed by one of the most popular artists in Florence today, Giorgio Vasari. On a flat stage set he painted a series of buildings with the Leaning Tower, the Baptistery and the Duomo appearing behind the houses.

The stage had a *"barrel vaulted ceiling, or 'sky' hung [with] a moving device of the passing sun. This was a mechanism with a gilded wooden lantern in the shape of the sun attached to it, with inside a crystal ball full of coloured water and two lit torches behind it which made it shine. A winch enabled the lantern to run slowly along an arch from one side of the stage to the other, behind and above the houses, giving the impression of the sun on its daily course from dawn to twilight."*[9]

After all these exhausting days of formality in Florence, we were finally left alone, and Cosimo took me to my now-favorite Poggio a Caiano.

This is perhaps one of the great love stories of the Renaissance. Cosimo chose Eleonora for her beauty, but she proved to be a true, intelligent, and devoted advisor to whom her husband listened all his life. They were always faithful to each other and constant companions. She supported her husband unhesitatingly in his policies and his trust was so great that in his absence he twice made her regent in his place. In 1540, Cosimo began the restructuring of Palazzo della Signoria. It had been built as a civic structure to house the offices of the business of the government.

Eleonora's new home in Palazzo della Signoria, the entry courtyard

Now Palazzo della Signoria was to become a home and accommodate an expanding family. Eleonora's prime duty was to give birth to heirs to the Medici line. Nine months and four days after the wedding, Eleonora at the age of seventeen, gave birth to the first of eleven children, a girl. Twelve months after that birth, the first of seven male children was born, Francesco, who was to become the successor to his father. Isabella was born one year five months after Francesco, Giovanni thirteen months later, Lucrezia one year and eight months later, then four boys in a row. Of those four boys, Pietro died at ten months to the day after birth, Garzia survived to die with his mother, in the Maremma, Antonio lived one day, and Ferdinando lived to become successor to Francesco.

Eleonora had been married ten years and one month and had given birth to nine children. Little Anna was born four years later and lived one day. Don Pietro was born one year after Anna, lived to be fifty, married a woman with the name of his mother, accused her of adultery, and strangled her with a dog leash.

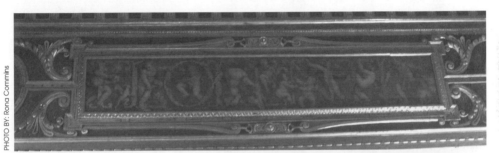

The letters of Eleonora's name are in the frieze at the top of a room of her apartment.

Entrance to Eleonora's apartments, seeming to hover above Salone dei Cinquecento.

1541: I am so excited to see the progress of our new home! Cosimo has hired Vasari to remodel the Palazzo della Signoria, and the first thing he is working on is a private chapel just for me. It will be on the *secondo piano* with my apartments. Cosimo wanted his apartments to be on *piano nobile*, because there he will be first to greet visitors. Vasari has torn out the old narrow staircases and now we will have a wonderful flowing grand entrance to upstairs where everybody lives. Cosimo's apartments will be at the top of the staircase next to the large meeting room, *Salone dei Cinquecento*.[10] When meetings are called, he will be able to walk through his entrance door directly into the Salone to be in attendance.

The children's rooms will be on the floor above mine. It will be immediately evident who is stomping around and throwing a fit! They will be able to play on the top floor of the Palace in the open loggias and get fresh air and sunshine without ever having to go down into the street.

Vasari tells me that the entrance to my apartments will be along the interior balcony which seems to hover in mid-air above the edge of *Salone dei Cinquecento*. I am to have my own little private study and my bedroom will be decorated with a gilded frieze above by the ceiling. This will be a whole new idea of decoration, letters of my name intertwined with *putti*[11] scurrying around through the letters. I can't wait to see it! The ceiling will tell the story of Esther, the Hebrew girl who was granted royal honor because of her virtue – at Cosimo's request. And my very own chapel! This will be in miniature, decorated by the greatest portrait artist of all time, Agnolo Bronzino.

1544: Eleonora moved into Palazzo della Signoria[12] with five children when the apartments were ready. Six more children were born while the family lived in that palace. Eleonora was considered by some to be an "overly religious Spaniard who refused to learn Italian." She invited the Jesuits into the city, this was a preaching order that brought the Inquisition into the city of Florence. The Jesuits were male evangelical preachers who practiced poverty, chastity, and charity, a communal order founded by St. Ignatius. Rule number thirteen of their order states: " . . . if [the church] shall have defined anything to be black which to our eyes appears to be white, we ought in like manner to pronounce it to be black."[13]

The Palace was still the town hall of Florence and its façade remained virtually unchanged throughout Cosimo and Eleonora's remodeling. It was the tallest building in the city until the Cathedral dome was completed and it was the bell of the Signoria which for centuries called citizens in times of trouble to assemble in 'Parlamento' in the square to be addressed by government officials from the Loggia dei Lanzi.

Eleonora and her husband each owned property independently. Her dowry of 50,000 Spanish ducats[14] was her own private fund. Eleonora purchased and sold real estate, loaned money, and traded in corn and foodstuffs. She purchased the Palazzo Pitti with the Bóboli Gardens as a summer villa, with her own money and full agreement of her husband. She paid 9000 gold florins[15] for it and bought it from members of the Pitti family. At that time the palace consisted of a central block with three arches,

*Piazza San Lorenzo, the piazza of the church where Eleonora di Toledo and Cosimo de'
Medici were married.*

seven windows above, and only two floors. The roof was missing, the Pitti did not have enough money to complete it. She also, in her foresight, bought up a lot of land round about and houses at the sides of the building with a view to its being enlarged.

Eleanora purchased houses, farm estates, and uncultivated lands. She bought marsh land, drained it, and when it became fertile, she sold or leased it. Near Grosseto she purchased the exploitation rights to Buriano Lake for herself and her children. It was sold to her by the city of Siena and she paid the lord of Piombino annual rent, then sold fish from the lake. She bought Florentine, Spanish and Neapolitan government bonds, and in Florence bought bank deposits to bequeath to churches and lay charities in her will. Annuities which she purchased for 50,000 *scudi*[16] yielded an annual income of 3,571 *scudi*, an increase of more than 6% per year.

Eleonora wore jeweled sumptuous clothes, and moved along streets surrounded by guards and servants. She had a litter built which she designed, lined in green satin and covered in velvet of the same color.

1545: I am so excited, Cosimo is commissioning Bronzino to paint a portrait of me in my favorite dress![17] It will include Giovanni, our two-year-old, whom we hope to make cardinal some day and maybe even Pope. Cosimo says this portrait will make

The gigantic Salone dei cinquecento in Palazzo Vecchio with Vasari's frescos of Florence "Triumphant in Battle" lining both sides of the room.

PHOTO BY: Rona Commins

a statement to the public about our respectability: "We are a nice stable normal family, place your trust in us."

The dress is a brocaded velvet with white satin background. In Spain we are proud of our fabrics, much of my dowry was beautiful textiles, but I have not seen anything like this in Spain. In Italy they call it *riccio sopra a riccio*, 'loop over loop', because the bouclé effect is made with gold threads wrapped in loops around the weft threads. The black pile arabesques[18] are in the shape of pomegranates – a symbol of fertility of course! Cosimo spoils me, he employs ten gold and silk weavers full time for my clothing.

I am also to get a new belt just for the portrait. An artist came into Florence the other day from Paris, a goldsmith named Benvenuto Cellini.[19] He is so famous in Paris that Cosimo has commissioned him for a new bronze to be placed in the Loggia of Piazza della Signoria where everyone can see it. It is to be an eighteen foot tall *Perseus*, taller than Michelangelo's *David*. Cellini claims he can cast it all in one piece so it will not have the color variations and the welded seams which mar Donatello's *Judith and Holofernes*. That will be interesting to see; every apprentice in Florence will want to work with Cellini to see if it can be done.

This Cellini is trying to finagle the commission for the *Neptune Fountain* away from my favorite sculptor Ammannati.[20] We shall see about that . . . it is a bit of intrigue that I will not allow! My new belt will be all of gold with jewels and beads and a golden tassel.

1547: There is a fire at the corner of Via della pergola and Via della Colonna, the home and workshop of Cellini are on fire! The whole roof is set to go and the *Perseus* is inside.

Cellini had been working hard with apprentices right up to the moment when he was ready to pour the molten bronze. He was ill with a very high temperature from the sheer effort of the work and because of the intense heat. There was a risk that the house would catch fire. Cellini was forced to go to bed and left his workers to control the casting. That is when the accident happened: the metal didn't melt down and the temperature was too high for the furnace. The lid exploded which set fire to the roof of the house. He was forced to throw ". . . all my tin plates and bowls . . ."[21] into the melting pot to lower the temperature and carry out the casting. He managed to get to sleep two hours before dawn. He'd solved the problem, the temperature of the furnace was down to normal, but he'd lost the roof of his house. Two days later he uncovered the statue: it was perfect except for three toes which he remade.

[The discovery of the quantity of tin used in the casting came to light in 1947 when, after the war, the statue was returned to its original place in the Loggia after being hidden in 1940. The restorer, Bruno Bearsi, analyzed the metal and it was discovered that the percentage of tin corresponded exactly to twenty-two English plates for which Cellini had requested reimbursement from the Grand Duke.][22]

1562: The last thing I was able to have made for my beautiful Eleonora was a large cameo.[23] The famous engraver of gems, Giovanni Antonio de' Rosso, began work on it in 1558, four years after our last child, Don Pietro, was born. I am depicted in profile, facing to the right, wearing my antique armor; Eleonora is portrayed mirroring me with her hair gathered in a pearl hair-net and an ermine stole on her shoulders. With her left hand she is holding our youngest child, Pietro, and he is playing with the sheepskin of the *Order of the Golden Fleece*, given to me in 1546 by Charles V. There was enough space on the shell for Rosso to include four more of our children behind our shoulders. Sadly this cameo was never to be finished because my beloved Eleonora died in 1562. It was intended that the center of the cameo be inlaid with a *pietra dura*[24] medallion carved in relief showing the towns of Tuscany. I hadn't the heart to have the cameo finished after Eleonora died.

When I asked Eleonora and the boys to go with me in 1562 to inspect the fortifications of Maremma, Leghorn, and Pisa in the fall of 1562, they agreed to go. I thought a change of scene would do us all good, and the milder climate after the heat of the Florence summer would be good for Eleonora who was suffering from the effects of recurring consumption.[25] Our three boys, nineteen-year-old Giovanni, fifteen-year-old Garzia, and thirteen-year-old Ferdinando were excited to go for a holiday. Doctors had warned me of a risk of malaria in those months in the Maremma district, but it couldn't happen to us.

The first one to get sick was Giovanni. Eleonora wore herself out caring for him. He died on 18 November 1562. Garzia died twenty-three days after the death of Giovanni and Ferdinando was in extreme danger. We kept the news from Eleonora. She died five days after Garzia. We buried her in the church of San Lorenzo in her beautiful pearl hair-net which she had worn for her cameo portrait, for Bronzino's portrait, and for our wedding.

The Bronzino portrait is a symbol of the ideal woman of the Renaissance. It tells of the fortune and riches Eleonora brought from Spain, "a beautiful young mother of high birth, who cemented the future of Florence through her children and the wealth she brought to the city."[26] Her royal castillian ancestors and her relation to the Hapsburgs gave the Medici a blue blood line which they had lacked, and put them on a strong foot with other European sovereigns. Before Eleonora, the Medici name had been in danger of becoming extinct.

1. "Medeateca di Palazzo Medici-Ricardi," www.palazzo-medici.it.

2. Poggio a Caiano, is a Medici villa 10 miles W of Florence.

3. *Primo piano* translates 1st floor in Italy but it is what we call 2nd floor. *Terra* is gound-floor, our 1st floor.

4. Palazzo Medici-Ricardi
   Via Cavour 3 (street name changed from Via Larga)
   Open Thurs-Tues 9:00-19:00 (Closed Wed)

5. San Lorenzo is located in Piazza San Lorenzo off the street Borgo San Lorenzo. A street named "Borgo" means that the street was outside the city walls. The terms coat-of-arms, crest, and *stemma* are interchangeable.
   San Lorenzo
   Open Mon-Sat 10:00-17:00
   Sun 13:30-17:00

6. Francesco Giambullari in a letter to Giovanni Bandini.

7. Ibid.

8. *Spettacolo*, a spectacular or exceptional performance.

9. Francesco Giambullari, op. cit.

10. *Salone dei Cinquecento* was a 13,000 sq. ft. room built in Palazzo Vecchio to house the new legislative body of the Republican government. The room was decorated by Vasari with views of Florence at war.
    Palazzo Vecchio ....Piazza della Signoria
    Open daily 9:00-24:00, to 19:00 in winter
    Thurs 9:00-14:00

11. *Putti* are male cherubic angels used as a decorative element.

12. Palazzo della Signoria took the name Palazzo Vecchio, "Old Palace", after 1549 when the Medici grand-dukes took up residence across the river in Palazzo Pitti.

13. *Wikipedia*, Society of Jesus.

14. A Spanish ducat was worth a little over $100 in today's currency. 3,000 Spanish gold ducats =$301,456.

15. One gold florin was worth $100 in today's dollars.

16. The scudo was a coin issued by the Papal States in Rome until 1866. When Italy was unified as the Kingdom of Italy in 1871 all cities began to use the same coinage, the lira. One scudo = 5.375 lira.

17. Bronzino's portrait of Eleonora is in the Uffizi in the *Tribune* room.
    Uffizi ....Piazzale Uffizi 1
    Open Tues-Sun 8:15-18:50 (Closed Mon)

18. Black was one of the most expensive dyes to make in the Renaissance, it was based on pigments brought from the New World.

19. Benvenuto Cellini is most famous for his golden "salt cellar" which is in the Kunsthistorische Museum in Vienna. It was made for Francis I of France. It was stolen in 2003, recovered in 2006.

20. Ammannati's *Neptune Fountain* was renamed *Il Biancone* by the people of Florence, a pejorative name meaning "Big Whitey". Michelangelo scoffing at the fountain, said *Ammannato, Ammannato, che bell' marmo hai rovinato,* "Ammannati, Ammannati, what a beautiful piece of marble you have ruined."

21. Benvenuto Cellini, *Autobiography*.

22. Information from Flavia Atzeni, "Perseus", www.catpress.com.

23. The Cameo of Cosimo and Eleonora with their family is exhibited in the **Museo degli Argenti**
    Museo degli Argenti..**Palazzo Pitti**
    Open daily 8:15-18:30, and to 19:30 June-August. ....Closed 1st and last Mon of the month
    Cumulative ticket #2 includes Boboli Gardens, Costume Gallery, and Porcelain Museum

24. *Pietra dura* is a work made of semi-precious hard stones such as carnelian, agate, jade. The Medici had a workshop just for producing pietra dura work.
    Museo dell' Opificio delle Pietre Dure ....Via degli Alfani 78
    Open daily 8:15-19:00 (Closed Sun)

25. The term *Consumption* meant tuberculosis.

26. **Christine Zapella, "Smart History."**

View of the courtyard of the new Offices (Uffizi), with the Palazzo della Signoria (Palazzo Vecchio) connected at the northeast end of the new Offices.

Chapter Six

More Offices

"The wish to acquire more is admittedly a very natural and common thing; and when men succeed in this they are always praised rather than condemned. But when they lack the ability to do so and yet want to achieve more at all costs, they deserve condemnation for their mistakes."

— Niccolo Machiavelli
1511 *The Prince*

"It is a great and good thing to know how to earn money, but it is even better to know how to spend it wisely. And to know how to retain and to guard that which has been left to you from your patrimony or by your relatives is superior in merit to the above mentioned virtues. For that which a man does not earn is easier to spend than that which he gains with his labor and sweat and care."

— Paolo Da Certaldo
1360 *Il libro dei buoni costume*

16 July 1576

Paolo Giordano Orsini notified me: "While washing her hair in the morning ... [my wife Isabella] was found ... on her knees, having immediately fallen dead."[1] The burial registry in the Medici church of San Lorenzo recorded the date, 16 July 1576. The registry also made note of the fact that Isabella's face was disfigured by asphyxiation and that there was a red mark around her neck, though her husband claimed apoplexy.

My sister Isabella was the third child of our parents, Cosimo de' Medici and Eleonora di Toledo. She was betrothed at eleven and married at sixteen to Paolo Orsini, who is the son of a powerful Roman family. It was a political marriage; father thought the Orsini family would be able to help protect our southern borders. Cosimo used his power during his reign to transform Florence's public institutions into a monarchy which became official when he was declared "Grand Duke of Tuscany," a title bestowed upon him by Pope Pius V. My father became the first Medici to be called Grand Duke. When father died two years ago, I as his first son, became Grand Duke Francesco.

Our sister Isabella always did have great freedom in our home in Palazzo della Signoria, much more freedom than was customary for a Florentine woman. Our older sister, Maria was never well and died at seventeen when Isabella was fifteen. I think father and mother allowed Isabella more freedom as a result. Isabella was the opposite of Maria, strong and healthy, vivacious and intelligent, father had her educated along with us boys by our private tutors. She learned to speak French, Spanish, and Latin; she was a musician, singer and poetess.

When Isabella married at the age of sixteen, it was not a happy marriage. Paolo Orsini was one year older than she, but he treated her in a tyrannical and cruel manner. Paolo's cousin fell in love with Isabella which was not surprising considering that she returned home to our home in Palazzo Pitti when our mother died. Isabella was twenty, and she never returned to her husband's home in Bracciano. A long-distance marriage suited Isabella just fine.

On 16 July 1576 Isabella had been living in Florence with our family in Palazzo Pitti for fourteen years when her husband, Paolo Orsini, appeared in Florence and invited her to the villa of a friend at Cerreto Guidi. She decided she had better go, since he was still her husband. It appears that when he bent over to give her a kiss, he slipped a noose around her neck. The cord passed through a hole drilled in the ceiling and in the room overhead Orsini's henchmen 'hoisted her up by force'. Orsini passed off Isabella's death as an apoplectic attack. People did not believe it, but the Orsini are a powerful family.

The story of how the *Uffizi* came to be is this. In 1560 our father hired Giorgio Vasari, the most well-known sculptor and painter in Florence at that time, to build more offices for government workers. It was becoming difficult for both government and family to co-exist in the same building. Our oldest sister, Maria, had already died and our youngest brother, Pietro, was only six. Our home, Palazzo della Signoria, had been the symbol of civic power in the city of Florence for more than two centuries before our family moved in. Now we needed a new building that would be big enough to hold the government offices and to exhibit our family treasures.

The *Uffizi*[2] project was completed in time for my wedding in 1565 to Joanna, the sister of Austrian Emperor Maximilian II. My father was contemplating connecting the palace in the Palazza della Signoria, with our 'summer palace' across the river in Piazza Pitti. In only five months Vasari was able to build an enclosed corridor which ran across the bridge of Ponte Vecchio and into the Boboli Garden of Palazzo Pitti. The first use of the 'Vasari Corridor' was for my wedding.

The *Uffizi* turned out to be an ideal space for the exposition of our Medici treasures. The long halls are perfect for sculpture. The rooms on *terra piano* (ground floor) are the offices and above, on the *piano nobile*,[3] (second floor) are the collections. The Room of the Maps for example, has paintings of all the possessions of Tuscany which are under the rule of Florence and also houses scientific instruments.

Vasari's grand new staircase created for Eleonora di Toledo and Cosimo in Palazzo della Signoria.

The Pharmacy room has apparatus to distill perfume, medicine and poisons, and there is a room with a collection of weapons from all over the known world.

My favorite room in the Uffizi is the theater. We used to have all our theatrical productions outside in the courtyard at Palazzo Pitti, and we had to cover the whole Pitti courtyard whenever the weather looked bad. Of course we can't flood the floor of the Uffizi and float ships in it as we did in the *cortile* of Palazzo Pitti, but the advanced stage machinery of the Uffizi's *Teatro Medici* makes up for it. Buontalenti designed the remarkable Uffizi Theater twenty years after the Uffizi opened, and we have used it ever since.

A performance in the *Uffizi Theater* is always impressive. The grand staircase conducts throngs at a time to the first landing in front of the three huge carved-panel doors of the theater entrance. Marble doorframes are surrounded by tall arches of grey *pietra serena* stone set in cream-colored plaster. Buontalenti has been influenced by Michelangelo in so many instances that it seems as though he were back from Rome, alive, and with us again in Florence.[4] The ceiling of the theater is so high that it extends up into the room above and we can see the beams where the flat scenery is attached to be lowered down onto the stage.[5]

Father retired from public life and named me his regent when I was twenty-three years old. He did not have much joy in continuing as ruler of Florence after the death of seven children in our family. Two of them died with our mother at Christmastime in the swampy Maremma region of Pisa. He was still willing and able to intervene in politics though, and he still retained the title of Grand Duke until his death. At forty-eight he had a cerebral hemorrhage, went into a complete physical and mental decline, and died at fifty-four.

I was able to improve things in our family properties. Nine years after mother's death I had an office *studiolo*[6] carved out of the side of the big government meeting room *Salone dei Cinquecento*. We changed the name of the palace to Palazzo Vecchio, Old Palace when we moved into the new palace in Palazzo Pitti. The Studiolo had no entrance at that time from *Salone dei Cinquecento*, the only entrance was from the rooms which had been my father's on that floor. I was very interested in natural sciences and alchemy and you can see that in the décor. Behind the lower row of paintings are secret cupboards for my treasures. The portraits below the end arches of the ceiling are of my parents, Cosimo I and Eleonora di Toledo. In back of the painted panels there is a small staircase which goes up to the little *tesoretto*, my father's private study.

The star of the whole Uffizi is the little red octagonal room which I had designed in 1584, the *Tribuna*. It contains the most precious pieces of our collection. The decorative subject of this room is the 'Theme of the Four Elements'. The ancients believed that everything in the universe was composed of four elements, Earth, Air, Fire and Water. In the Tribuna EARTH is represented by the floor of semi-precious stones; AIR is a weathercock pennant on the outside of the dome which connects to an inside pointer; FIRE is the red fabric which upholsters the walls; WATER is the

Eleonora di Toledo, the Spanish Princess, wife of Cosimo de' Medici. She is pictured with her son Giovanni at age two. He died with his mother Eleonora in the Maremma. Painted by the court artist Agnolo Bronzino.

Michelangelo's "Badalone," the ship which he invented to float large blocks of marble to Florence on the Arno River. The ship sunk on its maiden voyage.

A cabinet made of black ebony, Pietra dura inlaid semi-precious stones created in the Medici workshop of Opificio delle Pietre Dure.

(above) An Annunziation from the workshop of Andrea della Robbia, who used a ceramic process and glaze which is unknown to this day.

(left) Michelangelo's Laurentian Library in the cloister of San Lorenzo. Many came here to study architecture and Michelangelo's unusual, cut stone masonry, stair design.

Pietre dure cabinet with semi-precious stone inlay of agate, carnelian, lapis, jade, etc. This type of work was produced in the Medici workshop, Opificio delle Pietre Dure.

The studiolo which Francesco de' Medici created at the edge of the Salone dei Cinquecento. Eleonora di Toledo's portrait is in the end arch of the room.

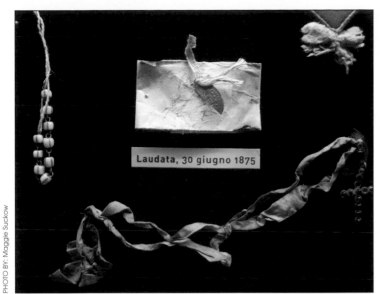

PHOTO BY: Maggie Suckow

Laudata, 30 giugno 1875

(left) The objects left with the last female orphan at the Spedale degli Innocente.

(below) Confirmation of the Franciscan Rule, *detail from left to right, Antonio Pucci, Lorenzo the Magnificent, Francesco Sassetti, and his son. Fresco from the Sassetti Chapel in the church of Santa Trinita, depicting Lorenzo's (Bob Hope) flattened nose.*

PHOTO BY: Rona Commins

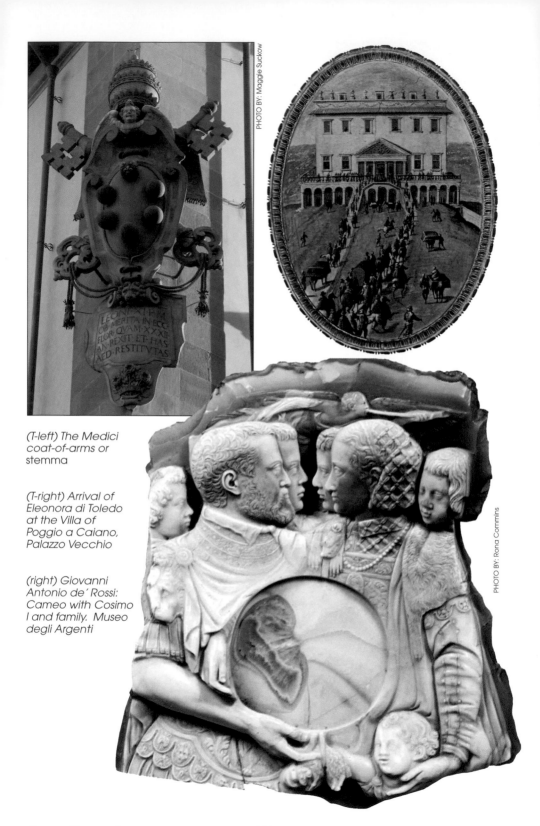

PHOTO BY: Maggie Suckow

(T-left) The Medici coat-of-arms or stemma

(T-right) Arrival of Eleonora di Toledo at the Villa of Poggio a Caiano, Palazzo Vecchio

(right) Giovanni Antonio de' Rossi: Cameo with Cosimo I and family. Museo degli Argenti

PHOTO BY: Rona Commins

PHOTO BY: Rona Commins

Piero di Cosimo: Simonetta Vespucci.

The ancient wall of 1333 which surrounded Florence on the south side of the Arno.

In the Campo of Siena at the Palio horse race. Left to right Judith Ruggles, Natalia Dutra, Rona Commins, Nancy Lee.

mother-of- pearl inlay of the dome. The creation of this little masterpiece is one of the great satisfactions of my life.

Lately I have learned the rest of the story about our sister Isabella and Paolo Orsini. During the time that Isabella was in Florence with us after our mother's death, her husband fell in love with Vittoria Accorambi who, it is said, 'wanted to be Princess of Bracciano.' After Isabella died, Vittoria and Paolo could not marry because Vittoria was still married. Then when Vittoria's husband died they still could not marry because Pope Gregory XIII forbid it. They remained in Bracciano but social pressure forced them to live outside society. When a new Pope was elected at the death of Gregory XIII, the new Pope was Sixtus V who was the uncle of Vittoria's dead husband. Things went from bad to worse, the couple fled to Venice and in a short time Paolo Orsini died. When Paolo left all his possessions to Vittoria, his family was in a rage. The Orsini family had Vittoria murdered six weeks after Paolo's death.

As we were growing up in Palazzo della Signoria, we had another Eleonora in our family: a cousin named Eleonora di Garzia di Toledo who grew up with us almost as another sister. Our pet name for her was Leonora or more often, Dianora. Dianora was mother's niece, the only child of Don Garzia di Toledo, a Commander-in-Chief of the Spanish Navy. Dianora's father was always at sea so she grew up with us. Isabella was eleven when Dianora was born and the two of them became inseparable companions at our house.

Our youngest brother Pietro was one year younger than Dianora and always tried to make some 'fun.' I can remember how he chased the girls around in the loggia or teased them unmercifully, hoping that mother would not hear in her rooms below. Mother and father were always worried about Pietro's cruel temperament. Dianora grew up to be so beautiful that it was said that she had eyes 'like two stars in her head.'[7]

Father wanted to keep the lovely Dianora in the family and so he married her to Pietro when they were eighteen and seventeen respectively. This turned out to be an unfortunate marriage because Dianora was never happy with the ill-tempered Pietro. She had flirtatious relationships and our brother Pietro strangled her with a dog leash. This happened 11 July 1576, five days before Isabella was strangled by her husband. These are called "crimes of honor," the kind of intrigue that can go on in Italian families. I can't really blame the men though.

18 February 1743

On this date the last Medici died, Anna Maria Luisa, wife of Johann Wilhelm, Elector Palatine of the Rhine. In her will, *Patto di Famiglia*, she left to Florence all the patrimony of the Medici family. She donated all objects in villas and palaces as well as the immense Medici wardrobe of sumptuous clothing used for major ceremonies to the city of Florence in perpetuity.

> *"The Most Serene Electress cedes, bestows and transfers*
> *... all the furnishings belongings and rarities ... such as galleries,*
> *paintings, statues, libraries, jewelry and other precious things, as*
> *well as saints' relics, reliquaries and their decorations in the Palace*
> *Chapel ... upon the express condition that it be maintained as or-*
> *namentation of the State, for public use and to attract the curiosity*
> *of foreigners, nor shall it ever be removed or transported outside of*
> *the capitol and the Grand Ducal State."*[8]

The people of the world continue to visit these treasures in Florence, a city which is a museum itself which would not exist if the patrimony of the Medici had been sold and disbursed throughout the world.

According to the Anna Maria Luisa's will *Patto di Famiglia*, no objects were ever to leave Florence. However in spring of 2009, the Medici *Chimera*, a 2,400 year old Etruscan bronze found in Arezzo in 1553, was exhibited at the J. Paul Getty Museum in Malibu, California, "The first time to visit the United States." Cosimo had claimed the bronze statue immediately when it was discovered in 1553 and had it installed in his home at Palazzo della Signoria.[9] It is now back on exhibit where it belongs, in the Florence Archeological Museum with other Medici treasures.

PHOTO BY: Maggie Suckow

The Chimera, Medici property which was never to leave Florence according to the will of Anna Maria Luisa de' Medici.

1. *Wikipedia*. "Isabella de'Medici."

2. The Uffizi art gallery ....Piazzale degli Uffizi 1
    Open daily 8:15-18:50 (Closed Mon)

3. *Piano nobile* is 2nd floor, the most prestigious location in the home. *Piano terra* is 1st floor or "ground floor."

4. Grey *pietra serena* stone, a fine-grained blue-grey sandstone quarried in Tuscany, contrasted with creamy plaster, was a characteristic of architectural design by Michelangelo.

5. The entrance to the Uffizi Theater is now the entrance to the "Drawing and Print Collection". The theater extended upward into what is now the Botticelli room.

6. Small spaces like the *studiolo* are viewable by pre-arrangement. Tickets for timed tours of the *Studiolo, Tesoretto,* and the attic above the Salone dei Cinquecento may be purchased in the museum office.

7. Blog: Raucousroyals.com

8. Anna Maria Luisa's Will is quoted from *The Medici, Story of a European Dynasty*, p.134.

9. latimesblog.com/culturemonster/2009

10. National Archeological Museum ....Piazza Santissima Annunziata
    Entrance on Via Caponi
    Open Tues-Fri 8:30-19:00
    Sat-Sun 8:30-14:00 (Closed Mon)
    Reservations for Accademia and Uffizi can be made here without standing in line.

Piazza Santa Croce

Chapter Seven

A Joust For Giuliano

*"Men ought either to be indulged or utterly destroyed . . . for if you merely
offend them they take vengeance, but if you injure them greatly they are unable
to retaliate, so that the injury done to a man ought to be such that vengeance
cannot be feared."*

— Niccolo Machiavelli
1511 *The Prince*

*"I urge and admonish you if you want to live in liberty never allow any citizen in
the republic to grow so great that he is more powerful than the laws. The appetite
of man is so insatiable that if a man is more powerful than is proper, the more he
will want and desire what is not legitimate."*

— Alamanno Rinuccini
1466 *Ricordi storici di Filippo di Cino Rinuccini*

29 January 1475

The trumpeters stand at the ready in Piazza Santa Croce. Giuliano de'
Medici is sure to be champion this year.

In Florence we always use Piazza Santa Croce for jousting; it is the largest piazza in Florence and will hold crowds of people. A huge rectangle of space like this can't be found anywhere else in the city. It is on the outskirts in what used to be marshland before the followers of St. Francis settled and started to build a church and monastery here two-hundred fifty years ago.

This morning I helped put up the 'tilt barrier' in the Piazza. It is an important part of the traditional set-up for a joust. When two horsemen with lances are riding toward each other at high speed and their object is to break each other's lances on the shield or armor of the opponent – or unhorse him – anything can happen. With the wooden passageway of the tilt barrier, the horse and rider are contained so they don't collide, and the lance is held at the correct angle to break the opponent's weapon.

The excitement is high this year because we're celebrating a new military alliance between Florence, Venice and Milan. Everyone will be showing off to the foreign

A joust at Monterigione, a small town within enclosing walls in the hills outside of Florence.

visitors – Giuliano himself has commissioned new jousting armor and a helmet made of silver from Verrocchio, one of Florence's greatest sculptors. When Giuliano's brother Lorenzo won the joust six years ago, his prize was a silver helmet and 10,000 florins.[1] Giuliano will begin this tournament already wearing a silver helmet.

A competitor in a joust rides onto the field preceded by his processional banner. For this joust Giuliano commissioned his processional banner from one of Florence's greatest artists, Sandro Botticelli. He chose a portrait of Simonetta Vespucci who had been elected 'Queen of Beauty' this year. Botticelli painted her on a blue ground, dressed as helmeted Pallas Athena wearing a breastplate and antique-style armor. An ancient French motto at the bottom of the banner states *La sans pareille*, "The one without equal."

The foreign mercenary leaders, *condottieri,*[2] and the knights have been in town for a week now. They are staying north of Florence in the outskirts at the convent of Santa Maria Novella where there is space for the horses and equipment. When we see these foreigners around town, we are astounded by their jewelry, fabric and armor. I know that Venice is known for brilliant colors and Milan for creative cuts of fashion, but we Florentines have always been known for our textiles. I've never seen so many different weaves and colors in combination as I have seen this week. It seems as though every man has a different tailor trying to outdo every other tailor.

Each man has his own cortege of mounted grooms and trumpeters all flaunting their apparel, harnesses and standards of superb quality and amazing workmanship.

The parade begins at the Cathedral square, Piazza del Duomo. First in line are the young noble Florentines with horses stamping and throwing up their heads, as impatient to show off their finery as their riders. Next come the pages on their horses, pennants flying, wearing family colors emblazoned with coat-of-arms, and helmets with spangles and feathers on top. All the foreigners march in groups interspersed with drummers and trumpeters, and children and dogs run alongside in packs taking part in the excitement.

Nothing can compare with our Giuliano! He presents himself at his best, the 'golden boy' of Florence. His phalanx of nine trumpeters announces his entrance; he sits like Mars on his brawny steed *Orso*[3]; his posture displays his superior horsemanship and his obvious skill in athletic exercises – master of hunting, running, and javelin throwing. *Orso* wears full armor today also, like his master. A caparison thrown over the horse's armor is elaborately embroidered with Giuliano's coat-of-arms. The iron head-shield protects the horse from lethal blows of the lance.

Giuiliano's armor shines spectacularly. The sun is full over-head and the preliminaries are complete. We are all watching Orso to see how he will stand up under the weight of a full coat of silver armor. Jousting armor is heavier than the plate armor which is used for war combat, it weighs twice as much and is much less specialized since it does not need to permit free movement as armor does for a knight on the field. The only limiting factor for jousting armor is the weight a horse can carry.[4]

On top of his silver armor, Giuliano wears a white silk over-shirt embroidered with pearls. It is sliced by a cut of red over his shoulder where he has thrown a bright-red cape with three-finger deep gold fringe tipped with 'big pearls, diamonds, rubies, and sapphires of enormous value.'[5] Giuliano's shield is covered with a half-kilo of pearls, all of which will be lost on the jousting field for spectators to pick up.

A contemporary observer, Giovanni Augurelli (1441-1524) wrote:

> *"You were the last to enter the field, o my Giulio, but the first in beauty, strength, and wealth. It is impossible the quantity of jewels and pearls that glittered on your person, on your company, and on your mounts: I cannot do justice to the lines of horsemen, footmen, and heralds, since, poor me, half out of my mind, I could not wrench my eyes from your divine form, covered in gems and diamonds: Mars in arms and Love in visage."*[6]

In this, his most famous joust, Giuliano chose to wear the colors of Simonetta Cattaneo, this year's 'Queen of beauty'. Courtly Love was at full tilt, and it usually involved love of a man for a married woman. The more unavailable she was the more desirable. Man was inspired by 'nobility and chivalry,' not physical love. It was said that Giuliano had fallen deeply and hopelessly in love. Simonetta was married to a family friend, Marco Vespucci, a Florentine and member of the parish of Ognisanti.[7] La bella Simonetta was beloved by all Florence for her beauty, modesty and piety.

29 January 1475 — The trumpets are sounding, let the *mostra* begin!

This year for sure we will see a *spettacolo*!

26 April 1476 — La bella Simonetta is dead.

Simonetta was protagonist in a brief but splendid season of Florentine public and private life. She died of consumption in 1476; her coffin was paraded around the city to show the fragile nymph; she was a real figure of urban myth, the most beautiful woman in Florence, cut down in the springtime of her life. She married at sixteen to Marco Vespucci, a relative of Amerigo Vespucci whose name christened America. They were married in Florence in the Medici Palace in Via Larga.[8]

Probably Botticelli painted Simonetta's portrait for the first time for the 1475 joust. From that time on, her face and figure seem to be the inspiration for his female figures including his most famous paintings of 1481-1483, *Spring* and *Birth of Venus*. This recurring classic beauty crowned with a mass of golden strawberry blonde hair is seen again and again in his work, from Madonna to nymph to Venus.

Was Simonetta Botticelli's muse, his inspiration of ideal female beauty? Or were the similarities in Botticelli's women just representative of the canons of beauty of the time? Was there more than just an artistic rapport between artist and muse? It is an intriguing question with an unknown answer. There is however one fact: when Botticelli died in 1510, he requested to be buried at Simonetta's feet in the Church of Ognisanti, parish church of the Vespucci.

1. To understand the value of 10,000 florins in Florence in 1475, it is interesting to note that the following year in 1476 the Medici sold Verrocchio's bronze *David* to the Signoria of Florence for 150 florins. It was placed in Palazzo della Signoria.
2. *Condottieri* were the leaders in the professional military.
3. An *Orso* is a bear.
4. Jousting armor weighs about 100 lb. Field armor for war weighs about 50 lb.
5. *The Florentine*, "Simonetta Vespucci, a Model of Renaissance Female Beauty" by Cristina Acidini.
6. www.swide.com/art "Simonetta Vespucci: Botticelli's Muse."
7. **The church of Ognissanti:** The 2nd altar on the right, painted by Ghirlandaio, shows the Vespucci family protected by the *Madonna della Misericordia*. Amerigo, the young boy portrayed to the left of the Madonna, gave his name to America following the path of his contemporary Christopher Columbus.
    Ognissanti .... Borgo Ognissanti 42
    Open daily 7:15-12:30, 16:00-20:00
    Sun 9:00-10:00, 16:00-20:00
    Refectory of Ognisanti which inspired the Last Supper of Leonardo da Vinci in Milan.
    Last Supper by Ghirlandaio
    Open Mon, Tues, Sat 9:00-12:30.
8. The Florentine, op. cit.

Chapter Eight

Galilei And The Opera

"Be very careful not to spend more than you possess. Every year seek to save one-fourth [of your income.] Do not forget to take into account extra-ordinary expenses which might occur, so that when they come, you will be able to meet them without touching your possessions or your patrimony . . . and since the family is continually growing, one must move ahead and save as much as one properly can. Watch carefully over the minor expenses outside of the home, for they are the ones which empty the purse and waste money . . ."

> — Paolo Da Certaldo
> 1360 *Businessman's Book of Good Advise*

"My lords, you must think I am not pleased with the Courtier if he be not also a musician . . . and have skill in like manner on sundry instruments. For if we weigh it well, there is no ease of the labors and medicines of feeble minds to be found more honest and praiseworthy in time of leisure than [music] . . ."

> — Baldasare Castiglione
> 1528 *The Courtier*

On Music: "Plato calleth it 'a divine and heavenly art.' Homer said musicians are 'worthy of honor and regard of the whole world.' Aristotle averreth music to be the only disposer of the mind to virtue and goodness, wherefore he reckoneth it among those four principal exercises wherein he would have children instructed."

> — Henry Peacham
> 1622 *The Compleat Gentleman*

14 December 1634

A letter from Pietro de' Bardi to his friend Giovan Battista Doni:

My father, Signor Giovanni, who took great delight in music and was in his day a composer of some reputation, always had about him the most celebrated men of the city [of Florence], learned in this profession, and inviting them to his house,[1] he formed a sort of delightful and continual academy from which vice and in particular every kind of gaming were absent. To this the noble youth of Florence were attracted with great profit to themselves, passing their time not only in pursuit of music, but also in discussing and receiving instruction in poetry, astrology, and other sciences.

The courtyard of Palazzo Pitti, scene of opera and theatrical performances for Medici entertainments."

Many stories were represented….and received with great applause
. . . The most famous of these stories were the Euridice and the Arianna;
besides these, many shorter ones were set to music by Caccini and Peri . . .

Predicting for Your Lordship a most happy Christmas, I pray
that God Himself, the father of all blessings, may grant Your Lordship
perfect felicity.

Your Very Illustrious and Reverend Lordship's
Most humble servant,Pietro Bardi, Conte di Vernio"[2]
(Florence, 14 December 1634.)

The protagonists:

1 Vincenzo Galilei,[3] a composer and lutenist, "the father of the present famous astronomer, a man of a certain repute in those days, who was so taken with this distinguished assembly that, adding to practical music in which he was highly regarded,
[he also studied]….musical theory."

2 Giulio Caccini, a singer and teacher of singing, who played lute, viol and
harp, "considered a rare singer and a man of taste, he was at this time in my father's
'Camerata,'[4] and feeling himself inclined toward this new music, he began, entirely
under my father's instructions, to sing ariettas, sonnets, and other poems."

3 Jacopo Peri who "received high praise as a player of the organ and the keyboard
instruments, and as a composer of counterpoint was rightly regarded as second to
none of the singers of that city."

4 Ottavio Rinuccini,[5] poet: "The first poem to be sung on the stage . . . was the
story of *Dafne*, by Signor Ottavio Rinuccini, set to music by Peri in a few
numbers and short scenes and recited and sung privately in a small room. I was left
speechless in amazement."[6]

5 Giovanni Bardi, host of the Camerata, soldier, writer and composer, patron of music
and the arts, father of Pietro de' Bardi.

6 October 1600

Rinuccini: "How are rehearsals going for our *Euridice*?"

Peri: "We haven't really had rehearsals yet. I will know more when we get
on stage. I'm singing the part of the hero Orfeo. I wonder how people
will like the new way of singing? They will be able to understand the
words of your libretto[7] better, that's for sure."

Caccini: "Well, you know that my daughter Francesca[8] is also singing in
Euridice. It's a little risky for her to be making her public debut at the

wedding celebration of King Henry IV of France and Maria de' Medici – but you know thirteen-year-olds."

Bardi: "I wonder what the acoustics will be like in the *cortile* of Palazzo Pitti?[9] You must tell us how it feels to sing there, and if you can hear your voice over the instruments."

Rinuccini: "I've seen that *cortile* used for theatrical productions, and it seems to me that flooding the courtyard and floating ships on it as I have seen done, would work better than a musical production like ours."

Bardi: "Vincenzo, have you heard any more about how your son Galileo is doing in Pisa?"

Galilei: "He has been up to his usual, experimenting and trying out new ideas. Now he is dropping things off the Leaning Tower to see if stones fall faster than feathers and if heavy stones fall faster than lighter ones."

Bardi: "Well, Galileo is thirty-six now, isn't it about time that he did something practical with his life?"[10]

Peri: "Giulio, I'm glad we decided to collaborate on *Euridice*. If we are going to 'improve modern music and raise it . . . from the wretched state to which it has been reduced'[11] we had better do it together. Two can take the public flak better than one."

Caccini: "Yes, we ourselves are taking a risk trying to bring back the ancient form of Greek-tragedy with sung dialogue, ensembles and choruses. Who knows if the performers can do it, let alone if the public will accept it. Just because we can sing in the new mode doesn't mean that others will be able to."

Rinuccini: "But it is not really that much of a risk if Royalty accepts it in Italy and France. If it is the newest form of entertainment everyone will want to go along with it."

Bardi: "I agree. When we put together *Dafne* and performed it privately for ourselves in this Palace three years ago, we had no idea that the Medici family would commission us to write another work in the same style for the wedding of their daughter to King Henry IV of France!"

Galilei: "Do you think it might rain on the 6th of October? It is pretty late in the year for an outdoor wedding celebration."

20 December 1600

Less than three months after the wedding performance of *Euridice* for the Medici in Palazzo Pitti, Giulio Caccini published a manuscript edition of his own version of *Euridice* eliminating Peri's songs and substituting his own. In an intrigue against Jacopo Peri, Giulio Caccini made a claim to be the sole inventor of the new

PHOTO BY: Rona Commins

(above) The palazzo on the right is the Palazzo Bardi where the Camerata met to create the first opera Dafne in 1598.

(right) A plaque was placed on the front of Palazzo Bardi to commemorate the writing of the first opera by the Camerata.

IN QUESTA CASA DEI BARDI
VISSE GIOVANNI CONTE DI VERNIO
CHE AL VALOR MILITARE
MOSTRATO NEGLI ASSEDI DI SIENA E DI MALTA
CONGIUNSE LO STUDIO DELLE SCIENZE E L' AMOR DELLE LETTERE
COLTIVÒ LA POESIA E LA MUSICA
E ACCOLSE E FU L' ANIMA DI QUELLA CELEBRE CAMERATA
LA QUALE INTESA A RIPORTARE L' ARTE MUSICALE
IMBARBARITA DALLE STRANEZZE FIAMMINGHE
ADLA SUBLIMITÀ DELLA GRECA MELOPEA
DI CUI SCRISSERO GLI STORICI DELL' ANTICA CIVILTÀ
APRÌ LA VIA GIÀ CHIUSA DA SECOLI
AL RECITATIVO CANTATO E ALLA MELODIA
E CON LA RIFORMA DEL MELODRAMMA
FU LA CUNA DELL' ARTE MODERNA

N. MDXXXII   —   M. MDCXII

A view of the interior courtyard of Palazzo Bardi.

style of singing and to be the first to bring it into print. In his dedication of his *Euridice* manuscript published 20 December 1600 Caccini wrote:

> *"I had thought, on the present occasion, to deliver a discourse to my readers upon the noble manner of singing, in my judgment the best for others to adopt, along with some curious points relating to it and with the new manner of passages and redoubled points, invented by me . . . I have reserved this for another occasion, enjoying, for the time being, this single satisfaction of having been the first to give songs of this kind and their style and manner to the press."*[12]

February 1601

Six weeks after Caccini's manuscript for *Euridice* went to press, Peri published his manuscript of *Euridice* which was the original score from the Medici wedding performance. It included music composed by him and music composed by Caccini. In the Foreword to the manuscript printed February 1601 (one year after Caccini's manuscript) Peri described the new manner of singing, gave credit to Caccini for his compositions included in the opera, and said "Caccini's was printed first but mine was performed first."

> *"Signora Vittoria Archilei . . . has always made my compositions seem worthy of her singing, adorns them not only with those groups and those long windings of voice, simple and double, which the liveliness of her talent can invent at any moment . . . but also those elegances and graces that cannot be written or, if written, cannot be learned from writing.*
>
> *"I had composed the work exactly as it is now published, nonetheless Giulio Caccini . . . composed the airs of Euridice and some of those of the shepherd and of the nymphs and of the chorus . . . These airs may be seen in his* Euridice, *composed and printed only after mine was represented before Her Most Christian Majesty."* [13]

On 5 December 1602 Giulio Caccini's *Euridice* which had been published two years earlier had its first performance in Palazzo Pitti.

1. On Palazzo Bardi there is a marble plaque commemorating this palace as the meeting place of the Camerata and the creation of the first opera.

   On the corner of Via de' Benci and Via dei Neri (Not open for visitors)

2. Oliver Strunk, *The Baroque Era*, " Pietro de' Bardi Letter to G. B. Doni," p.3. The Bardi family in 1320 commissioned Giotto to paint the frescoes of St. Francis in the "Bardi Chapel" in the church of Santa Croce. The Bardi Chapel where Michelangelo and others came to sketch is the 1st chapel left of the altar.

   Santa Croce ....Piazza Santa Croce
   Open daily 9:30-17:30
   Sun 14:00-17:30

3. Vincenzo Galilei was the father of the astronomer Galileo Galilei.

4. *Camerata* is an Italian noun meaning chamber or room.

5. The Rinuccini Palazzo: A marble plaque on the wall commemorates Rinuccini as the poet of the first operas. Across the street is a marker from 1333 showing the height of the flood that year.
   Palazzo Rinuccini ....On the corner of Via dei Neri and Via de Rustici
   (Not open to the public)

   Rinuccini Chapel ....In the sacristy of Santa Croce
   Houses the robe of St. Francis and music manuscripts

6. Oliver Strunk, *The Baroque Era*, "Pietro de' Bardi Letter to G. B. Doni," pp.4-5.

7. A *Libretto* is the text for a musical stage work such as an opera or Broadway show.

8. Francesca Caccini (1587- c.1641) singer, composer, lutenist, poet, music teacher, was born in Florence. She became the best-paid musician at the Medici court, and was one of the best-known and most influential female composers of Europe. The King of France described her as the best singer in the world and requested the teenaged singer to be his court musician. The Medici refused to allow her to stay in France. Francesca spent all her life in Florence but traveled widely as a guest singer and composer. She was the first woman to write an opera, *La liberazione di Ruggiero* (1625). It was presented at the court of Prince Segismondo in Warsaw, the first Italian opera to be performed in Europe.

9. A *cortile* is the enclosed center courtyard of an Italian Renaissance residence. Palazzo Pitti, entry requires a ticket, but you may view the cortile for FREE from the entry queue.

   Piazza Pitti 1
   Open daily 8:15-18:50 (Closed Monday)

10. In 1592 Galileo was a professor of mathematics at the University of Padua. In 1633, Galileo Galilei was brought before the Inquisition and forced to recant his teaching that the earth revolves around the sun. After his death he was buried in a closet-sized room under the campanile outside of the church of Santa Croce. As a heretic he was not allowed to be buried inside a church. Ninety-five years later, with the exoneration of a new Pope, Galileo's body was exhumed and reburied inside Santa Croce in a place of honor opposite the tomb of Michelangelo. Galileo's right index finger is preserved in a special case and is exhibited in:

    Museo Galilei e Istituto di Storia della Scienza ....Piazza dei Giudici 1
    Open daily 9:30-18:00
    Tues 9:30-13:00.

11. Oliver Strunk, *The Baroque Era*, "Pietro de' Bardi Letter to G. B. Doni," p.4.

12. Oliver Strunk, *The Baroque Era*, "Giulio Caccini Dedication of Euridice", p.11.

13. Oliver Strunk, *The Baroque Era*, "Jacopo Peri Foreword to Euridice," pp.15-16.

Chapter Nine

Home For The Orphans

"Seeing how that the women of Florence wear garments cut out of divers cloths and robes trimmed with silk and of many fashions, with fringes and pearls, and often with buttons of silver gilded, four or six rows of them, sewn together in pairs, and with buckles of pearls . . . hereby is made provision and order concerning these matters: no woman shall wear either crown or wreath . . . nor pearls or precious stones, nor silk . . . nor petticoats and robes of two colors, and all trimmings are forbidden . . . and all this was done without giving a thought to the losses suffered, particularly by the silk merchants and jewelers.

My lords, all the days of my life I studied to learn the rules of the law, and now, when I did believe myself to know somewhat, I do find that I know nothing. For when . . . I went out to seek for the forbidden ornaments of your women, they met me with arguments the like of which are not to be found in any book of laws . . . My notary findeth one wearing many buttons in front of her dress, and he saith unto her, 'Ye are not allowed to wear these buttons.' But she answereth, 'Yea, Messer, but I may for these are not buttons, but studs, and if you do not believe me, look, for they have no loops, and moreover there are no button-holes.'

'Man proposes and women disposes,' a very old proverb as we all know; and that without ever having studied jurisprudence the Florentine women understood very well how to have their will and wear their fashions in spite of all the laws and doctors of laws!"

— Franco Sacchetti
1324 *Sumptuary Laws of Florence*

18 August 1419

T he Silkworkers Guild, *Arte della Seta*, began construction on a vast tract of land bought at the favorable price of 1,700 florins.[1]

In 1333 Florence had completed a new set of walls to greatly expand its enclosed territory. It was expected that the city would grow to fill the space. But the Florence population of 90,000 was steadily diminishing, first because of a disastrous flood in 1333, followed by a 'pestilence' in 1340 with 15,000 dead, and then by the Black Death in 1348 which killed off half of the remaining population. In 1419 there was much empty space near the church of Santissima Annunziata.

> *"Giorgio, can you believe it? I've heard they are going to build something on that big piece of land out there by the church of Santissima Annunziata."*[2]

"The loggia of Brunelleschi's Spedale degli Innocente, orphanage for foundlings, considered to be the first building of the Renaissance.

"Really Franco? There has been nothing there but empty fields for seventy-five years, since the last city walls were built before the plague."

"I hope they don't think someone will want to buy a house way out there, you never know what these modern real estate guys will think of next —"

Eight months later, Filippo Brunelleschi, honorable member of the guild *Arte della Seta*, was awarded the title of capomaestro (foreman) for construction of the new foundling hospital, *Spedale[3] degli Innocenti*.

"I hear the silk guild has hired that Filippo Brunelleschi as architect for their new orphanage. I wonder why they think he can do the job – as far as I know he's never worked as an architect before."

"I'm wondering the same thing. Brunelleschi lost that competition with Ghiberti for the doors of the Baptistery even though they were both trained as goldsmiths. That was twenty years ago and Brunelleschi hasn't done anything since."

"They say he's been in Rome studying Roman architecture."

Nine months months after Brunelleschi won the contract, the first column of the loggia of *Spedale degli Innocenti* was raised.

"Giorgio, I'm sure glad you brought me out to see this. Why would Brunelleschi be putting up columns? That's such ancient Roman stuff."

"Well Maria, maybe after all that time he spent sketching ruins down in Rome, that's all he can think of."

"I wonder how the Silk Guild will be able to pay for this. How did they even get the money to buy this huge piece of land?"

"Franco and I have been here quite a lot, talking to the workmen. They say that a guy from Prato named Francesco di Marco Datini left the Seta 1,000 florins in his will to build an orphanage. That's the money they used to buy this property."

"And I guess Brunelleschi is a member of the Silk Guild, that's why he got the contract?"

Francesco Datini chose to leave his bequest to the silk guild *Arte della Seta*,[4] a civic institution, rather than to a religious institution. The Seta was one of the wealthiest guilds in the city and like most guilds took upon itself philanthropic duties. As early as 1294 the Republic of Florence had named the silk guild as protector and educator of the city's abandoned children. Because of growing prosperity due to expanding trade, the guild members decided in 1419 that it was their civic duty to construct an orphanage. To finance the Spedale,[5] the Silk Workers taxed themselves one cent for every lira-worth of spinning and weaving of silk, and two cents for every lira-worth of work using imported silk

21 February 1421, one month after Brunelleschi began to build at the new Santissima Annunziata work site, "The architect Filippo Brunelleschi received his first payment for the orphanage to be called Spedale degli Innocenti."

PHOTO BY: Maggie Suckow

The rota, rotating wheel, installed in 1660 to receive babies into the orphanage.

"Franco, will you look at that? Look what this guy has accomplished in one month! Those arches between the columns must be at least eight meters high."

"Have you looked at the Cathedral lately? When Brunelleschi won the competition for building the dome on the Cathedral at the same time that he started building the Spedale here, I was sure he couldn't work on both projects at the same time. It's a good thing the opening on the Cathedral wasn't ready for the dome yet."

"Well, you'd think that after a hundred years of being open to rain and bird shit, it would have been ready!"

When the wool guild, *Arte della Lana*, had held a competition in 1419 to build the cupola[6] on the Duomo, two goldsmiths, Brunelleschi and Ghiberti had been the chief competitors. With the Spedale under his belt, Brunelleschi won the competition. In 1294 when the Cathedral was begun, no one in Italy knew how to build a dome, and the Florence dome was supposed to be the largest in the Western world, even larger than the Pantheon in Rome.

Back at Piazza Santissima Annunziata, it took the Florence 'Building Permit Department' over a year from the time that Brunelleschi had received his signed contract and had begun work on the *Spedale* until the work was officially "approved" and recorded: "The Council of the People of the City of Florence approve the proposal of *Arte della Seta* to build a new hospital, *Spedale di Santa Maria degli Innocenti*, with a vote of 233 in favor, 27 against. The *Spedale* is to be dedicated exclusively to the care of those children . . . who are commonly called foundlings . . . whose fathers and mothers, against the law of human nature, have deserted them . . ."[7]

"The city council sure took a long time to officially approve this work going on for the new orphanage. The building really looks amazing, doesn't it? With the columns and the arches, it's as close as you can get to Rome without actually being there."

Maria thought for a moment, then said, *"Well, I think it only echoes Rome without imitating it. I think it is a whole new archi-tecture, it's nothing like anything that I've seen anyway."*

"Well," Franco replied, *"I say there's something to be said for Florence's narrow streets that keep us out of the sun in the summer and the rain in the winter. This new piazza at Santissima Annunziata is going to be the biggest in Florence — no place to escape the July heat here!"*

The long loggia of Spedale degli Innocenti in the outskirts of Florence was a rare sight to see. People came from everywhere to watch the work in progress, gaping in wonder at the stately columns with capitals and graceful arches holding up the

The shadow of Brunelleschi's Dome covers all of Florence's people.

architrave of the roof, unheard-of architecture in that day-and-age. How could slender columns hold up all that long expanse of roof? All sides of the piazza were open spaces at first. The church of Santissima Annunziata added her foyer-loggia later in order to keep up the symmetry of the square. And just a few blocks south, there was that construction site of the Cathedral with its impossible dome.

By 1429 the body of the *Spedale* and the walls of the *Spedale* church were completed. The population of Florence was 37,000, nowhere near its pre-plague high of 90,000. With alternating years of sickness or poor harvests, economic difficulties stopped work on the *Spedale* construction site. Similarly, on the Cathedral site in 1429 there was a reduction in the workforce to keep down construction costs. It was time for Brunelleschi to begin the brickwork structure of the dome.

"Maria, I'm sure glad you could come to the cathedral with me today. This will really be something to remember, Brunelleschi is starting to lay the first layers of bricks for the dome."

"I know Giorgio, but how do you think he will do it? People say he is planning to build two domes, one inside the other, like he saw in the Pantheon when he was down in Rome."

Giorgio replied, *"Well, I'm just glad they finally finished bringing in the marble for the base of the dome. How does Brunelleschi think he will fit a round dome on an octagonal drum anyway?"*

"Bringing in those marble blocks made such a mess" said Maria. *"They had to float the stones up the Arno River from Pisa and land them by the bridge at Piazza del Pesce,[8] then haul them all the way across town to the Cathedral. I thought I would never see the end of the dust!"*

"Did you ever get to see that boat Brunelleschi invented to float the marble to the Florence? He called it Il Badalone,[9] and he

PHOTO BY: Rona Commins

even patented the monstrous thing! It used wind mills to turn cog wheels to move paddles to propel the ship. He did not want to be paid for the invention but wanted a commission for each load of cargo that it carried."

"Yes, I heard about that fiasco, the thing sank on its first voyage! Just think what that invention cost him."

Brunelleschi's Death Mask is preserved in the museum Opera del Duomo.

Brunelleschi proposed to build the dome with two layers of brick, one dome inside the other. The traditional method for building a dome was to build a scaffolding strong enough to support the workers and the materials, then build a wooden frame the shape of the dome to hold the bricks which were placed on top of the framework. The mortar of the time took several days to set and that would put extra strain on the scaffolding.

But the big problem was that there were no trees long enough and strong enough, or in plentiful enough supply to use the traditional technique. Brunelleschi proposed to lay the bricks of the cupola in an interlocking herring-bone pattern with reinforcing rings of steel and wood added as he progressed upward. Even Brunelleschi did not know for certain if his plan would work. He was on the job daily to watch the shape of the bricks and the angle that they were laid.

There were also other on-the-job issues to be addressed. Brunelleschi had won the competition, Ghiberti had lost. But the cautious *Opera del Duomo* committee overseeing the cathedral construction, "to be on the safe side," had appointed both Brunelleschi and Ghiberti together as co-supervisors with equal pay. Ghiberti had his own independent fame with his doors and Brunelleschi wanted his own fame with his dome! How was he going to be able to get Ghiberti off the job? With a bit of intrigue on his part, Brunelleschi, solved the problem.

> *"Oh Maria, here is the latest scandal, Brunelleschi has got Ghiberti off the job! Remember how they were always giving each other malevolent looks?"*

> *"Yes, and Brunelleschi always thought that Ghiberti had no idea what was going on anyway – and they were both being paid the same."*

> *"Oh Maria, I wish I had been there to see it! A few days ago, Brunelleschi took to his bed 'sick' and Ghiberti had to take over. It was a crucial moment in the job, the scaffolding had to be moved and a reinforcing ring of wood or stone had to be placed at the same time. Ghiberti had no idea what to do next, and now the* Opera *has taken Ghiberti off the job, and Brunelleschi is celebrating!"*

Ghiberti's name was never mentioned again in documents as co-capomaestro of the Cathedral dome. In order for Brunelleschi to do the job he was hired to do on the dome, he had to invent the machinery to do it: a crane to hoist very heavy material up continually increasing distances; an apparatus with wheels and cogs to change the up-and-down direction of the moving machine without having to take the ox out of harness and turn it around; a ship to transport marble from Pisa.

In 1436 when the Duomo dome was completed and the three domes of the surrounding tribune were ready to be roofed with terra-cotta tiles, Brunelleschi was hired as manager of the construction project. His surprisingly modern contract stated:

100 florins for his time
400 florins for expenses – 100 more than he had asked for
Cost overruns to be paid out of his own pocket
A guarantee that the roofs would not require repairs for 25 years

The Spedale took longer than the dome to build. Twenty-five years after work began on 5 February 1445, the Spedale degli Innocenti opened as a foundling hospital. Ten days later the first infant was retrieved from the basin, the *pila*, placed at the front portico to received abandoned infants. The pila became the symbol of the institution. The Spedale at first accepted only newborns and foundlings. They came from the city as well as the country and were normally abandoned by their parents because of war, high grain prices, destitution and illness. Females were abandoned more frequently because poor parents could not afford a dowry.

Records show that the Spedale degli Innocenti in its first three years of existence from 1445-1448 received 260 children. In 1448, Brunelleschi had been dead for a year and the plague returned to Florence. The deaths numbered 30,000-50,000 depending on which source you choose to read. The Spedale children were recorded as being "washed with strong vinegar" to ward off plague.[10] It was also in that year that a new altar painting was dedicated in the church of the Spedale

On 28 October 1485 Ghirlandaio signed a contract for an *Adoration of the Magi* for the church of the Innocenti. The contract specified that it be a panel painting on wood, it would be completed in thirty months, it was to be painted by his own hand not the "workshop of Ghirlandaio," it must use "precious colors" with the paints paid for by Ghirlandaio himself. He must use four ounces of the most expensive lapis lazuli blue (which had to come to Europe from Afghanistan on camels.)

> *"Hey Maria, remember how busy it was out at Santa Maria Novella with Ghirlandaio, his brothers and his whole bottega working on that huge set of frescoes of the Life of Mary and John the Baptist behind the main altar?"*

> *"Yes, they have only been working on it for two months, but they sure have accomplished a lot in that amount of time. I'm really excited to see what Ghirlandaio will give Michelangelo to paint. I'm sure he wouldn't trust a thirteen-year-old new apprentice with the Virgin Mary scenes that include the donor's daughter and friends."*

> *"Well, you will never believe this Maria, but Ghirlandaio has signed another contract to paint at the same time. He will be doing an Adoration of the Magi for the Spedale degli Innocente, a really big altar painting to be done in thirty months! He will be portraying rich silk merchants adoring the new-born baby Jesus at one end of town, then run over to Santa Maria Novella at the other side of town to work on Tornabuoni's daughter at the birth of the Virgin Mary."*

The cloister of the Spedale degli Innocente.

Documents of the orphanage in 1560 record the presence of four-hundred fifty resident children with eight-hundred seventy other children out in the country with wet-nurses. When babies first arrived at the orphanage, they were wrapped round and round in long cloths "so that they would not injure themselves." These are portrayed in the famous blue and white della Robbia plaques which were installed above the portico in 1487. The Spedale boys were taught to read and write, then were placed as apprentices with an artisan workshop. Girls were taught sewing and cooking, and the majority either became nuns or were married with dowries supplied by the institution. Many remained on in the service of the Hospital. In the *Madonna of the Innocents* painting in the museum of the Spedale the girls of the orphanage can be seen lined up: swaddled babies in front followed by girls to the age of twenty-five dressed in white, those to forty-five dressed in blue, and those beyond the age of forty-five dressed in black.

It was difficult to find as many wet nurses as were needed; women from the city and the country and servants from the wealthier homes of the city were paid a modest salary. "Outsiders" (wet nurses) are listed in the records, and there were one-thousand thirty-six children listed as given out to the care of foster families. From the beginning legal adoption was encouraged. In 1577 when Grand Duke Francesco was visiting the Spedale, he was told of the shortage of wet nurses. "In a trip to Spain," he said, "I saw cows kept just to feed babies." A cow was brought to the Spedale and their milk was "given to the children in special little glasses with teats."[11] This is the oldest written record of artificial nursing.

Ultimo, 30 giugno 1875

PHOTO BY: Maggie Suckow

The half-medal which was left with the last baby received in 1875 at the Spedale. His given name was 'L'ultimo', 'The Last One.

A new method of receiving children into the Spedale was begun in 1660. A *rota* was built in the north end-wall of the portico. This was a rotating horizontal wheel that brought the baby into the building without the parent being seen. Babies and older children could thus be left anonymously. The number of children left kept growing, and in 1699 a metal grate was placed on the "wheel" to stop delivery of older children. The steps up to the rota and the closed-up opening are still in existence on the north end of the portico at the Spedale degli Innocente.

By 1774 there were over nine-hundred children admitted to the Spedale every year. A mortality rate of 83% was reported; the most common cause of death was smallpox. The first experimental vaccination was performed here in 1756. In 1822 the Istituto Vaccinogeno Toscano (Tuscany Institute of Vaccinations) was installed in the Spedale complex and from here all Tuscan provinces were supplied with vaccine.

On 30 June 1875 the last two children were passed through the grate of the Ospedale. It often happened that an abandoned child was left with a memento from their family – a religious medal, a note, a lock of hair, a locket. Sometimes these were a way to let the child know that they had been left with love. Sometimes this was a method for the child to be recovered if the family fell upon better times. It would be something which could be cut in half, with half left with the child and the other half retained by the family. The last two babies who were received at the Spedale on 30 June 1875 came with a half- medal each and a note saying they had been christened. They were sent to wet nurses in the country and were retrieved by their parents after they had been weaned. Their legal names given them by the orphanage were:

Male: Ultimo Lasciati – "The Last One Deposited"

Female: Laudate Chiusura – "Praised Conclusion"

1. The florin, also known as *Fiorino d'Or* of the Republic of Florence, was the first European gold coin struck in sufficient quantities to play a significant commercial role. First minted in 1252, it became the standard currency throughout most of Europe. It was a mark of prestige and a better deal to be paid in florins.

    Florence had a second currency, the silver soldi. In 1252 thirty soldi was equivalent to one florin. The value of the soldi declined 1400-1432 until instead of 30:1 the value became 77-83:1. There was also the lira which was a 'shadow currency.' One lira = 20 soldi or about ¼ florin. This was an abtract denomination used for accounting purposes. The value of the lira fluctuated but the florin never did, it always held its value. It was a payment in gold which would theoretically have the same value the day it was promised, the day it was paid, and the day it was spent. Workmen were paid and everyday goods were purchased in lira, soldi, and denari. The denari was a copper coin worth 1/12 soldi.

    The coinage of other countries fluctuated in value against each other. The florin was a common measure of value for foreign exchange transactions. Banks of Florence were international with branches across Europe. The florin was minted 1252-1533, there was no change in design or content=54 grains of pure gold or $200 in modern currency. The design of the florin was a fleur-de-lis surrounded by the word 'Florentia' on one side and St. John the Baptist, patron saint of Florence, in a hair shirt on the other side.

2. The church of Santissima Annunziata, a functioning parish church, is an important destination for weddings in Florence. It is customary for brides to lay the wedding bouquet on the altar here.

    Santissima Annunziata ....Piazza Santissiama Annunziata

    Open 16:00-17:50 for visits, frequent masses throughout the day

3. Spedale is a word in an old Tuscan dialect for Ospedale. Today it is called Ospedale degli Innocente. It was the first orphanage in Europe for foundlings.

    Ospedale degli Innocente..Piazza Santissima Annunziata
    Open Mon-Sat 10:00-16:00
    Sun 10:00-14:00

4. In Renaissance Florence it was necessary to be a member of a guild to be a citizen with voting rights and to conduct any kind of business. There were 21 guilds: 7 "great guilds" and 14 "lesser guilds". The economic and political power rested in the four guilds which dealt directly with big business: Calimala (merchants), Lana (wool manufacturers), Seta (silk manufacturers), and Cambio (bankers). From these four guilds came most of the political leaders and the sponsors of art and construction to beautify the city and glorify the guilds.

5. From Attilio Piccini *Spedale degli Innocenti, The Foundling Hospital and its Museum*, p.8
    "The Innocents" are the children of Bethlehem who were massacred by King Herod in his effort to eliminate the new-born King of the Jews. The Spedale is arguably the first work of Renaissance architecture. The room which is now the museum was the recreation room for the children of the orphanage.

6   A *cupola* and a *dome* are synonymous. A Duomo and a Cathedral are synonymous. A cathedral houses a *cathedra* or seat of a Bishop, any Catholic church without a Bishop is called a basilica. Within a city, only one church can have a chair of a Bishop and be called a Cathedral. A Duomo does not necessarily have a dome.

7. Attilio Piccini *Spedale degli Innocenti, The Foundling Hospital and its Museum*, p.5.

8   Piazza del Pesce is off Via Por Santa Maria, it is the piazza in front of the church of Santo Stefano. There was a fish market here, possibly even in Roman times. The loggia for the fish market was torn down by Cosimo when Vasari built the corridor over the Ponte Vecchio for the wedding of Eleanora's son Francesco.

9   A model of Brunelleschi's *Badolone* may be seen at the ticket office for the Cathedral museums in Pizza del Duomo. Ticket office is on the street N of the Duomo. Brunelleschi had written the first copyright in history: no one else was allowed to copy his ship, and if someone did build one, Brunelleschi's contract required that the ship be burned.

10. Attilio Piccini *Spedale degli Innocenti, The Foundling Hospital and its Museum*.
11. Ibid.

Chapter Ten

A Most Holy Church

"In his latter days Cosimo fell into an irresolute mood and would often sit for hours without speaking, sunk in thought. In reply to his wife who remarked on his taciturnity he said, 'When you propose to go into the country, you trouble yourself for fifteen days in settling what you will do when you get there. Now that the time has come for me to quit this world and pass into another, does it not occur to you that I ought to think about it?' "

— Vespiano Da Bisticci
1470 *Vite di uomini illustri del secolo XV*

"Si stava meglio quando si stava peggio," We were better off when we were worse off.

— Ancient Tuscan Saying

17 January 1439

In 1439 an Ecumenical Council of the Catholic Church was held in Ferrara. The purpose was to heal the schism between the Roman and Eastern Orthodox churches, neither of which, though both of them were Christian, could agree on basic tenants of the Christian faith. On 17 January 1439 the Council was moved to Florence because of plague in Ferrara. During the "Council of Florence," as it came to be known, entertainments were held for the visiting dignitaries.

The Council ended in failure, no agreement could be reached. But Brunelleschi was a great success. He was commissioned to design and create elaborate stage machinery for religious plays which went on during the time that the members of the Council were in Florence. One of these plays was performed in the church of Santissima Annunziata,[1] in the piazza where the project of building the orphanage had begun eighteen years before. Thousands of people were to see Brunelleschi's "new style of architecture" at the Spedale degli Innocenti.

A Russian Orthodox Bishop, an eye-witness to a Sunday religious play in Santissima Annunziata, described angels flying through the air and fire sent by God the Father with a noise like thunder:

The Piazza Santissima Annunziata with the loggia of the church on the right.

"Fire comes down ever more abundantly and noisily from the upper tribune and sets ablaze the candles in the church though without burning the clothing of the spectators or doing them any harm. When the angel has returned to the point from which he descended the flame ceases and the curtains close again."[2]

The delegates to the Council of Florence also saw in Santissima Annunziata, besides religious plays, hundreds of life-sized wax images called *voti*.[3] Pilgrims who came to the church to venerate the miraculous painting of the *Annunciation*[4] often left votive offerings of wax. The painting had been begun in the 1200s by one of the monks but he abandoned it in despair because he did not feel he could create a beautiful enough image. It was supposedly completed by an angel while he slept. This painting was placed in the church and became so venerated that in 1444 the Gonzaga family from Mantua financed a special tribune to house it.

Santissima Anunnziata gave the right to the powerful men of the city, as well as distinguished foreigners, to erect *voti*, "thank offerings" of themselves in the church. These life-sized wax images were dressed in real clothes. Many were life-sized models of the donor, some even with full-sized horses. Andrea Verrocchio, the sculptor who made Giuliano de' Medici's armor for the 1475 joust in Piazza Santa Croce, produced these waxworks on a massive scale. Lorenzo de' Medici ordered three wax figures of himself from Verrocchio after the assassination of Giuliano in Florence Cathedral in

1478. One of Lorenzo's wax voti was placed in Santissima Annunziata, it was wearing the clothing Lorenzo had worn on the day of the attack.

In 1516 a special atrium was built to house the waxes: *Chiostrino dei Voti*, "Little Cloister of the Votive Offerings." After the nave became full of waxes, images were hung from the ceiling with cords and threatened to fall down on the heads of the faithful.

> *"By 1447 there were so many [of these votive offerings] it became necessary to stand these figures in an orderly manner in the nave. There they obstructed the view of those in the side chapels, particularly because some wax figures were seated on horseback in full armor."[5]*

A document of 1488 states that wax voti were to be banned from the church. By the late 1700's there were six hundred images and Santissima Annunziata became one of Florence's great tourist attractions. In 1786 the wax voti were melted down to make candles.

The building across from the Spedale, designed by Antonio da Sangallo the Elder, was given a Brunelleschian facade of a long, columned-loggia in the 1520s. The facade of Santissima Annunnziata, also made to imitate the facade of the Spedale, was added to the church in 1601 to define the eastern side of the piazza. The organ which dates from 1628 is the oldest organ in Florence and the second oldest in Italy.

29 June 1600

Preparations are fully underway for the wedding of Maria de' Medici to Henry IV of France. In three months, 6 october 1600, the performance of the new *spettacolo* titled *Euridice* composed by the Florentines Giulio Caccini and Jacopo Peri, will be held in the courtyard of Palazzo Pitti. On 29 June, Maria de' Medici, the future Queen of France, was witness to the birth of a new name-sake cousin born in Palazzo Pitti, Maria Maddalena de' Medici. The fathers of the two Marias were brothers. Unfortunately Maria Maddalena was born "malformed in the limbs" and was never able to walk well or climb stairs.[6]

1620 in Piazza Santissima Annunziata

> *"Luisa, how many years have you been living here at the Spedale? My parents left me as a baby and I doubt that I will ever see them. The people here are the only family I have ever know."*

> *"I am eight now, Anna, that's how long I have been here, two years less than you. Have you seen the new building they are putting up next door to our orphanage? It looks really big and I think it is a new palace – they say it might be for the Medici family. I don't know why the Medici would need another palace though, when they have the one on Via Larga, the one in the Signoria, and the Pitti across the river."*

"Have you ever been across the river to see that Palazzo Pitti out there in the country? I am ten and I have never seen it."

"We are lucky to even see this one, Anna!"

1621 in Piazza Santissima Annunziata

"Luisa, Luisa, come and look! A carriage is pulling up with the new girl who is going to live in the Medici palace next door. Do you think she is a Medici Princess?"

"Look at that, Anna, she can't even walk right! She is wearing beautiful clothes, but she sure has to hold onto someone and drag herself along to get anywhere. She looks about twenty years old to me."

"Well, she will be going to church in the Annunziata for sure and we will get to see her when we go to church there. I was wondering why the walkways were built in such a strange way, going in and out of the palace with overhead walkways into the Spedale and into the convent and even one that crosses the street from the palace to the Annunziata."

"I bet we won't get to see her at all, Anna. That must be what all those corridors are for, so no one can see her."

Maria Maddalena de' Medici lived in Palazzo della Crocetta, a palace purpose-built for her, from the age of twenty-one to thirty-three when she died and was buried in the convent of the Crocetta. Maria's mother took her at the age of nineteen to see the sea at Pisa and Livorno before she was installed permanently in her palace. She never took monastic vows, but lived here out-of-view of the public all her life.

Inside the church of Santissima Annunziata, the grill behind which Maria Maddalena de' Medici would sit to hear mass.

The Palazzo della Crocetta is now the National Archeological Museum.[7] The Medici Corridor which leads from the palace to the church of Santissima Annunziata houses an exhibition of Etruscan and Roman coins which is open only for special exhibitions. The palace was inaugurated as a museum in 1870 when Italy was united by King Vittorio Emmanuele. It contains the *Chimera*, the Etruscan bronze statue discovered in Arezzo in 1553 and purchased by Cosimo de' Medici to be placed in his home at Palazzo della Signoria. It is a mythological beast with a lion's head and body, with a goat's head on its back and a serpent's tail. An inscription in Etruscan on its rear leg says *Tincsvil* meaning "gift" or "offering."[8]

> *"Oh Luisa, remember when they tore that big hole out up in the wall of Santissima Annunziata? Up there, to the right, just as you walk in? It looks to me like that grill that they put up there lines up with that overhead passageway that goes across the street from the Annunziata to the palace."*

> *"That is why we never see her – she hears her own pivate Mass from her own private balcony."*

> *"I think this is an intrigue of the Medici family to prevent the city from knowing that one of their family was born with deformed limbs."*

1. Santissima Annunziata, the word "santissima" translates "most holy." The church of SS Annunziata is the third oldest church in Florence dating from 1248, after Santa Maria Novella in 1221 and Santa Croce in 1228. Florentine brides still go there today to lay their bouquets before the altar of the 1252 *Annunciation*.

   Santissima Annunziata ....Piazza Santissiama Annunziata
   Open 16:00-17:50 for visits
   Mass said frequently throughout the day

2. Walker, Paul Robert. *The Feud that Sparked the Renaissance*. 2003. Perennial. p.196.

3. A *votive offering* is an object left at a church in thanks for a cure, blessing, etc. It can also be a petition for a blessing, cure, etc. It is often in the shape of the thing desired or cured, made of silver, paper, leather, etc.

4. A painting of the *Annunciation* depicts the angel Gabriel announcing to Mary that she is to become the mother of God.

5. Andreas Quermann, *Ghirlandaio*," Waxworks in Florentine Churches."

6. It is speculated that Maria Maddalena had rickets, a vitamin D deficiency. Though well fed as children of the aristocracy, children were weaned early and saw little sun light. The fad for white skin kept them out of the sun. The skin was also whitened with sun-blocking cosmetic preparations.

7. National Archeological Museum - The Medici Corridor may be visited by special request.

   Piazza Santissima Annunziata ....Entrance on Via Caponi
   Open Tues-Fri 8:30-19:00
   Sat-Sun 8:30-14:00   (Closed Mon)
   Reservations for Accademia and Uffizi can be made here without standing in line.

8. This is the statue which was exhibited in the Getty Museum in Malibu California in 2009, against the express will of the Medici family *Patto di Famiglia* which stated that the Medici donation was conditional: No Medici property was "ever to be removed or transported outside of the capitol and the Grand Ducal State."

Interior of the church of Santissima Annunziata. In the right upper corner is the tabernacle which houses the Miraculous Painting of the Virgin Mary.

Chapter 11

Guide To Concerts In Florence

All Information Listed Is In Walking Distance Within Florence
(Exception: Fiesole With City Bus And Verona With Excursion)

Street Addresses In Florence Are Listed With Color Number: *R (Red) business, B (Blue) residential. R and B numbers run in numerical order within their color, there isn't a numerical relationship of R To B*

Very Useful Information: *Keep up with whats happening in Florence by reading the bi-weekly* The Florentine *www.theflorentine.net. For fun, inexpensive and educational day and week-end excursions, go with* Florence For Fun *www.florenceforfun.org.*

Summer Music Series

Orchestra Da Camera Fiorentina
March – October 9:00pm
M̄ Giuseppe Lanzetta, Director

Auditorium Santo Stefano Al Ponte Vecchio
Via Por Santa Maria Near Ponte Vecchio
Various: Symphony, Concerto, Opera, Ballet, Classical, Some Popular American

Musica Al Bargello
Courtyard Of Museo Nazionale Del Bargello ....Via Del Proconsolo 4
Various: Symphony, Concerto, Piano With Instruments

Museo Di Orsanmichele
Museum Above The Church ....
Entrance from Palace Of The Wool Guild next door.......................Via Calzaiuoli 13
Tickets at the door on day of Concert & at Orsanmichele ticket office:
10:00-13:00, 15:00-19:30
Segreteria Dell'Orchestra • Tel./Fax 055783374 • Email: Info@Orcafi.It

Orchestra Della Toscana
Museo Di Orsanmichele
Above The Church Of Orsanmichele...Via Dei Calzaiuoli 13

Auditorium Santo Stefano at Ponte Vecchio......................................Via Por Santa Maria
Tickets One Hour Before The Concert At The Door
Presale: Box Office: Via Delle Vecchie Carceri 1, Mon-Fri 9:30-19:00, Sat 9:30-14:30
Tel. 055 210804 • www.orchestradellatoscana.It

Santa Maria De' Ricci, Free
Via Del Corso, E Of Via De' Cerchi
Various Concert Events: Visiting Choirs, Chamber Ensembles
Evening concert events: posted on a poster at the corner of Via dei Calzauioli & Via del Corso

St. Mark's English Church, Free
Via Maggio 16-18
Afternoon performances of visiting choirs, etc.
Email: administrator@stmarksitaly.com • Web: www.stmarksitaly.com

Toscana Classica Associazione Di Produzione Musicale Della Toscana
Mᵒ Giuseppe Lanzetta, Director
May-Oct In Various Venues 9:00pm
Email: info@orcafi.It • www.orcafi.it

Opera

Maggio Musicale Fiorentino April-June, International Festival
Teatro Communale ....Corso Italia 16
Tel. 39 055 2779 350 • Email: infoboxoffice@maggiofiorentino.com
www.maggiofiorentino.com

Opera In Verona, Day Trip From Florence
Roman Arena, Verona
May-August
With Florence For Fun ....Via Della Pergola 10a/R
Tel.(+39) 0552476605 Office • Cell (+39) 3287290848
Email: travel@florenceforfun.org • www.florenceforfun.com

St. Mark's English Church
Complete Opera Performances 8:30pm
Concert Of Italian Opera Duets 9:15
Daily April-July

Via Maggio 18, Tickets At The Door Before The Performance
Advance Tickets & Info: (Int+39) 340 811 9192
Email: info@concertoclassicl.Info • www.concertoclassico.info

Chiesa Di S. Monaca
Concert Of Opera Arias ....Via Di S. Monaca 6
March-October
Mon, Wed, Fri, Sun 9:15pm
Tickets at the door on the day of the concert from 6:00pm
Booking tickets and info: 329.7843935

Organ Concerts

Cathedral Of Santa Maria Del Fiore
Various
Tel. 055.2302885 • wwwoperaduomo.firenze.it

La Badia Fiorentina (Florence Abbey)
1558 Zefferini Organ
Via Del Proconsolo, Entrance On Via Dante Alighieri
Monastiche Gemeinschaften Von Jerusalem

Santa Maria Assunta In The Badia Fiorentina
Tel/Fax: 055 264402 • Email: Gerusalemmefirenze@Tiscali.It
Visits of Church and Cloister of The Oranges
Mon 3:00-6:00 Pm

I Mercoledi Musicali Dell' Ente Cassa Di Ripsparmio Di Firenze
Il Grande Organo Di Clement Terni 1974
March-December 9:00pm On Wednesdays
Auditorium Ente Cassa Di Risparmio (Bank).................................Via Folco Portinari 5/R
Reservations And Info: Tel. 055.538.4012
Solo Organ, Organ Concerto, Harpsichord/Organ (with Gustav Leonhard)

Santa Maria De' Ricci
Via Del Corso, E Of Via De' Cerchi
Daily 9:15pm– Free Organ Concerts
Other concert events are posted at the corner of Via Dei Calzauioli & Via Del Corso

Mass

La Badia Fiorentina (Florence Abbey)
Via Del Proconsolo ....Entrance Is On Via Dante Alighieri
Monastiche Gemeinschaften Von Jerusalem
Santa Maria Assunta In The Badia Fiorentina
Tel/Fax: 055 264402 • Email: gerusalemmefirenze@tiscali.It
Laudes Tues-Sat 7:00, 12:30 Noon Service
Vespers 6:00pm • Eucharistico Sun 8:00 , 11:00
Visits of Church and Cloister of The Oranges: Mon 3:00-6:00pm
All services are preceded by 30 minutes of silent prayer

Chiesa Di Ognisanti (Church of Vespucci and Botticelli Families)
Piazza d'Ognisanti
Daily 8:00
Sun 10:30, 12:00
Roman Rite 6:30pm

St. Mark's English Church ....Via Maggio 18
    Church Of England, Diocese Of Europe
    English Church in the Palazzo for over 125 years
    Sung Mass every Sun 10:30am
    Church or Priest (Intl=39) 055 294764 • www.stmarksitaly.com

Cathedral Of Santa Maria Del Fiore
    Piazza Del Duomo
    Tel. 055.2302885 • www.operaduomo.firenze.it
    Mon-Sat 7:30, 8:30, 9:30, 6:00pm
    English:
        Sat 5:00pm
        Sun 7:30, 9:00, 10:30, 12:00, 6:00pm
    Vespers 5:15pm
    Baptistery: 10:30

Music Theaters In Florence

Teatro Comunale ....Corso Italia 16
www.maggiomusicale.com • Tel. +39 0935 564767

Opera di Firenze ....Viale Fratelli Roselli 1
www.operafirenze.it • Tel. +39 055 27791

Teatro Goldoni...Via Santa Maria 15
    Tel. 055.2779350 • www.maggiofiorentino.it
Teatro Goldoni ....Via Goldoni 83
    Tel. 0586.204290 • www.goldoniteatro.it

Teatro Della Pergola..Via Della Pergola 12/32
Tel. 055.0763333 • Email: pubblico@teatrodellapergola.com • www.teatrodellapergola.com

Teatro Verdi ....Via Ghibellina 99
    Tel. 055.212320

Auditorium Cosimo Ridolfi — FREE — Concerts Of The Music School
    Banca Credito Firenze, Bank ....Via Carlo Magno 7
    Tel. 055.597851 • www.scuolamusica.fiesole.fi.it

Aula Magna Del Nic ....Largo Brambilla 3
    Tel. 055.580996 • www.agimusfirenze.it

Piccolo Teatro Comunale ....Corso Italia 16
    Tel. 055.717270 • www.temporeale.it

Box Offices In Florence

For Concert Tickets in general *(Easiest To Buy At The Door Before The Concert)*

Box Office: Via Delle Vecchie Carceri 1
Tel.055210804 — All Florence Concerts
Tues-Sat 10:00-7:30pm
Mon 3:30-7:30pm

Box Office: In Florence For Programs In Fiesole,
Via Faenza 139/R
Tel. 055/210804 • Fax 055/213112 • Boxoffice.Fi@Alinet.It
Email: Info@Florencedance.Org • www.florencedance.org

Transportation: Concerts In Fiesole, Bus #7
Get On The Bus At Florence Bus Stop "San Marco" In Piazza San Marco.
Ride Up The Hill To The End Of The Line In Fiesole.

Teatro Romano Di Fiesole In The Roman Amphitheater
Entry is at the main square of Fiesole where the bus stops.
9:30pm in July
Ballet, Orchestra, Ensembles, Italian And International

Music School In Fiesole FREE
Various Venues • www.scuolamusica.fiesole.fi.it

Cultural Programms

British Institute of Florence
Palazzo Lanfredini ....Lungarno Guicciardini 9
Sept-June, Wednesdays at 6:00pm Lecture
8:00pm Talking Picture
Each Talking Picture Season takes a specific theme or personality from the World of Cinema: brief spoken intro based on prepared handout, screening of film, informal follow-up discussion

Tea With The British
Tea and snacks, newspapers and books
Every Thursday at 4:30pm • Tel. +39 055 2677 8270
Email: Library@Britishinstitute.It • www.britishinstitute.it

Movie Theater

Odeon Firenze, English and Italian Films
www.Odeonfirenze.Com
Piazza Strozzi • Tel. +39.055.214068
Segreteria +39.055.295051

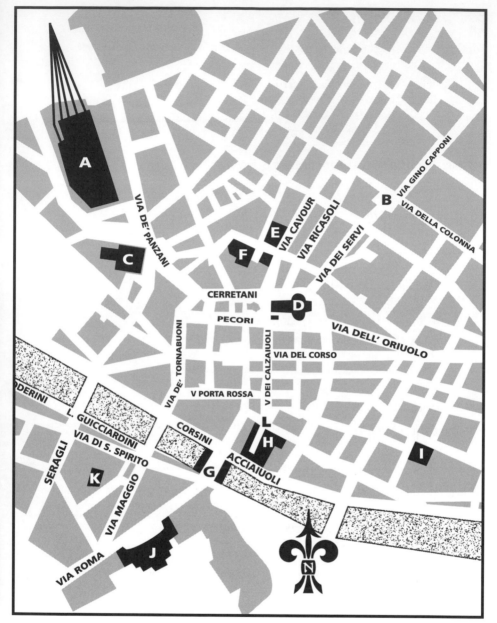

Walking Map of Florence

A Stazione Centrale
   (Santa Maria Novella Train Station)
B Piazza Santissima Annunziata
C Santa Maria Novella
D Duomo (Piazza del Duomo)
E Palazzo Medici-Riccardi
   (Medici Palace)
F San Lorenzo

G Ponte Vecchio
H Uffizi
I Santa Croce (Piazza Santa Croce)
J Palazzo de' Pitti
K Santo Spirito
L Piazza della Signoria

Acknowledgements

The Genesis of this book began many years ago with the person where all things begin, mother. I had flown to the last possible opera audition and had heard the dreaded words, "You are too old." Mother said, "Go to Florence." It was possible. My husband was on sabbatical from a Jr. High School teaching job and we flew off on the great adventure – to study in Europe. We spent the summer at La Poggerina, a monastery in the hills outside of Florence, operated as a school-of-the-arts for the University of Northern Colorado. So my first thanks go to my mother who gave me the chance to choose to study art and music. As a child of ten I was taken to oil painting lessons with Leola Hacken who taught me not only how to paint, but told me about the lives and histories of the great artists of the world. Leola made my grandmother's treasured book of famous paintings come alive to me.

Then, thanks to my husband who bought a Vespa moped that summer of 1977 in Italy, we could ride illegally two on the saddle down the hill from the monastery to the little train which took me daily into Florence. I boarded a public bus for the uphill trip to Fiesole, got off at the Villa Schifanoia Graduate School of the Arts, and was immersed in Tito Gobbi Master Classes. Everyday for six weeks in Florence, I fell in love: with the city, the culture, the language. Professor Paolo Barucchieri of Northern Colorado University, teaching at La Poggerina inspired me to "see the extraordinary in the ordinary" as his 2012 obituary reported. I spoke with Paolo in 1977 about teaching in Florence, little realizing that eleven years later almost to the day I would be a partner in founding a new Florence summer study program.

Ray Vernon had faith in me, believing that I had the knowledge and the charisma to help him start a summer school in Florence. Up to that time O.I.L., Opportunities in International Learning, had only functioned out of Paris. This was 1988, before the Exxon Valdez oil spill of 1989 changed our acronym to the more socially acceptable title of ACCENT International. Ray and I worked together in a hole-in-the-wall office with a borrowed typewriter, no email, no computers. I sat at Dr. Alberico's feet to study Dante and walked the streets of Florence with Linda Reynolds for art visits.

Accent grew from fifteen students to hundreds, took on Professor Rocky Ruggiero as Art Historian, and I continued to learn the language, the culture, the art and to teach the fascinating stories of Florence through the music of the Renaissance. Thank you Ray, Dr. Alberico, Linda and Rocky! In 2011, with the budget cuts in the California State University system, and after twenty-four years of teaching the program, summer foreign study programs were cut state-wide. This was when I began to collect my stories with the goal of publishing this book – I never knew the amount of work involved! Thanks to Daniela Grosso of ACCENT Florence for getting me on Facebook, to Kevin Hansen without whom I would still be ten-years-behind-the times on computer usage. Kevin always had time to PATIENTLY explain what I needed to know. My readers were invaluable: Judith Ruggles, Jacque Wright, Dena Erickson, Craig Kubey for his editing expertise, and many others who have checked out bits and pieces, friends both in the States and Italy.

When I realized that I would never make my deadline of the July 2014 Mu Phi Epsilon International Convention at the rate I was going, I stopped EVERYTHING. That is when thanks are really due, to all those who stepped in and left me with time to concentrate solely on THE BOOK: Richard Commins and Tav Commins who cooked and cleaned, Matthew Commins who completed the Bibliography, Rachel Hansen and Brittany Commins who picked up on the chores. And thanks to Linda Middlesworth of Caliornia Family Fitness without whose thrice weekly exercise class I would never have survived months of sitting at the computer.

Mary Chapeau, your graphic art expertise has put the finishing touches to this book and led it to the finished product which it is today. We met the deadline together. Without your constant encouragement and knowledge of the publishing trade this book would not exist.

Maggie Suckow and I spent twenty-five days together in Florence in 2013, I researched, she photographed. Thank you Maggie for your professionalism, and our wonderful days together. Your photos have greatly enhanced this book.

Thanks to the people who returned with me to Florence time again because they were as fascinated as I was: Kenneth Hutchinson-Surette, "Gino" Eugene Lee, Emily and Jean McPhie, Alice Langlois, Mimi Budd, Leo DiVita, Sally Weisbecker, Laurie Bell, Judith Ruggles, Janette Coffing, Barbara Baker, Tuyet Truong, Carol Urbani, Maggie and Lowell Suckow, Sharla Freeman, Kathy Hillier, Stephanie Hayden, Karyne Richardson, Maria Workman, De Ellsworth, Joanne Donatelli, Elizabeth Biggert, June Gable, Gloria Mayer, Joan Vorpahl, Sigrid Lennert. You were all people who shared with me more than once, walking with me through the Renaissance for a short summer of our lives. Thank you.

I have never lost the excitement of being in Florence where music and art and science began, learning more, seeing it anew. Here in Volume One is a taste of it for you!

INDEX

Bibliography

Accidini, Cristina. "Simonetta Vespucci, a Model of Renaissance Female Beauty." The *Florentine*. Web. issue no. 163/2012/may 10, 2012.

Alexander, Ronald, and Richard Savino. *Francesca Caccini's Il Primo Libro Delle Musiche of 1618: A Modern Critical Edition of the Secular Monodies*. Bloomington, IN: Indiana Univ., 2004.

Alighieri, Dante. *The Divine Comedy*. Trs. John D. Sinclair. Vol. 1-3. London: Bodley Head, 1948.

Appelbaum, Stanley. *The Triumph of Maximillian I*. 1964.

Ashley, Maurice. *The Golden Century: Europe, 1598-1715*. London: Phoenix, 1969.

Ausoni, Alberto. *Musica in Arte*. Mondadori, 2005.

Austin, Stephen F. "Like the Squawk of a Capon' – the Tenor Do Di Petto." *Journal of Singing* 61.3 (2005): 309-13.

Atzeni, Flavia. "Perseus." www.catpress.com

Barbier, Patrick. *The World of the Castrati, the History of an Extraordinary Operatic Phenomenon*. Trs. Margaret Crosland. Souvenir, 1998.

Baxandall, Michael. *Painting and Experience in Fifteenth Century Italy: A Primer in the Social History of Pictorial Style*. Oxford: Oxford UP, 1988.

Beck, Sydney, and Elizabeth E. Roth. *Music in Prints*. 1965.

Bell, Nicolas. *Music in Medieval Manuscripts*. Toronto: U of Toronto, 2001.

Binski, Paul. *Medieval Death, Ritual and Representation*. British Museum, 2001.

Boccaccio, Giovanni. *The Decameron*. Trans. Mark Musa and Peter Bondanella. Penguin, 2002.

Bowles, Edmund A. *Musical Ensembles in Festival Books, 1500-1800: An Iconographical & Documentary Survey*. Ann Arbor, MI: UMI Research, 1989.

Bragard, Roger, and Ferdinand J. De Hen. *Musical Instruments in Art and History*. New York: Viking, 1968.

Capretti, Elena. *The Building Complex of Santo Spirito*. Florence: Biblioteca De "Lo Studiolo", 2008.

Cardini, Franco. *The Medici Women*. Firenze: Arnaud, 1997.

Cellini, Benvenuto. *The Autobiography of Benvenuto Cellini*. Trs. John Addington Symonds. Penguin, 1961.

Cennini, Cennino. *The Craftsman's Handbook: The Italian "Il Libro Dell' Arte"* Trs. Daniel Varney. Thompson. New York: Dover, 1954.

Certaldo, Paolo da. *Il libro dei buoni costume ed.* by A. Sciaffini, "The Outlook of an Early Renaissance Businessman." Florence: Felice Le Monnier. 1945.

Cesati, Franco. *The Medici: Story of a European Dynasty*. Firenze: La Mandragora, 1999.

Cole, Bruce. *The Renaissance Artist at Work: From Pisano to Titian*. New York: Harper & Row, 1983.

Crabb, Ann. *The Strozzi of Florence: Widowhood and Family Solidarity in the Renaissance*. Ann Arbor: U of Michigan, 2000.

Duby, Georges. *A History of Private Life, Revelations of the Medieval World*. Trs. Arthur Goldhammer. Harvard UP, 1988.

Fanelli, Giovanni, and Michele Fanelli. *Brunelleschi's Cupola: Past and Present of an Architectural Masterpiece*. Firenze: Mandragora, 2004.

Ferguson, George. *Signs & Symbols in Christian Art: With Ill. from Paintings of the Renaissance*. New York, NY: Oxford UP, 1961.

Fornaciai, Valentina. "Toilette," *Perfumes and Make-up at the Medici Court: Pharmaceutical Recipe Books*, Florentine Collections and the Medici Milieu Uncovered. Livorno: Sillabe, 2007.

Fortune, Jane, Linda Falcone, and Andrea Bonadio. *Invisible Women Forgotten Artists of Florence*. Florence: Florentine, 2009.

Guidotti, Alessandro. *La Badia Fiorentina*. Firenze: Becocci, 1982.

Hale, J.R. *Encyclopedia of the Italian Renaissance*. Thames and Hudson, 1992.

Hall, James. *Dictionary of Subjects and Symbols in Art*. London: J. Murray, 1974.

Hamel, Christopher De. *Medieval Craftsmen: Scribes and Illuminators*. London: British Museum, 1992.

Hibbert, Christopher. *Florence: The Biography of a City*. New York: W.W. Norton &, 1993.

Holt, Elizabeth G. *A Documentary History of Art*. Princeton, NJ: Princeton Univ. Pr., 1981.

Innocenti, Clarice, and Cristina Acidini Luchinat. *Caterina E Maria De' Medici, Donne Al Potere: Firenze Celebra Il Mito Di Due Regine Di Francia*. Firenze: Mandragora, 2008.

Kaborycha, Lisa. *A Short History of Renaissance Italy*. Upper Saddle River, NJ: Prentice Hall, 2011.

King, Ross. *Michelangelo and the Pope's Ceiling*. New York: Walker, 2003.

Landucci, Luca, and Jodoco Del Badia. *A Florentine Diary: From 1540 to 1616*. London: Dent, 1927.

Larner, John. *The Lords of Romagna; Romagnol Society and the Origins of the Signorie*. Ithaca, NY: Cornell UP, 1965.

Law, Joe K. "Alessandro Moreschi Reconsidered, A Castrato on Records." *Opera Quarterly* 5 (1984): 1-12.

Lesure, Francois. *Music and Art in Society*. University Park: Pennsylvania State UP, 1968.

Levey, Michael. *Florence: A Portrait*. Cambridge, MA: Harvard UP, 1996.

Machiavelli, Niccolo. *Florentine Histories*. Tr. L. F. Banfield and H. C. Mansfield. Princeton, 1988.

Machiavelli, Niccolo. *The Prince*. Tr. Anthony Grafton and George Bull. Penguin Classics, 2003.

Martines, Lauro. *April Blood: Florence and the Plot against the Medici*. Oxford: Oxford UP, 2003.

Micheletti, Emma. *The Medici of Florence: Family Portrait*. Florence: Editrice Giusti Di S. Becocci & C., 1993.

Mignani, Daniela, Allesandro Conti, and Antonio Paolucci. *The Medicean Villas by Giusto Utens*. Florence: Arnaud, 1995.

Musacchio, Jacqueline Marie. *Art, Marriage, & Family in the Florentine Renaissance Palace*. New Haven: Yale UP, 2008.

Norwich, John Julius. *The Italians: History, Art, and the Genius of a People*. New York: Abrams, 1983.

Papafava, Francesco. *Spedale Degli Innocenti: The Foundling Hospital and Its Museum*. Florence, Italy: Becocci, 1977.

Phillips, Clare. *Jewels and Jewellery*. London: Victoria and Albert Publications, 2003.

Pisani, Rosanna. *Palazzo Davanzatti*. Florence: Giunti, 2011.

Quermann, Andreas. *Domenico Di Tommaso Di Currado Bigordi Ghirlandaio: 1449-1494*. Koln: Konemann, 1998.

Rinuccini, Alamanno. "Ricordi" in Filippo Rinuccini, *Ricordi Strorici*. Florence: 1840.

Roberts, Mark. *Street-names of Florence*. Firenze: Tipografia Coppini, 2001.

Rognoni, Gabriele Rossi. *La Musica Alla Corte Dei Granduchi: Guida Alla Mostra; Music at the Grandducal Court*. Firenze: Giunti, 2001.

Strano, Giorgio. *Galileo's Telescope: The Instrument That Changed the World*. Firenze: Giunti, 2008.

Strong, Roy C. *Splendor at Court; Renaissance Spectacle and the Theater of Power*. Boston: Houghton Mifflin, 1973.

Strunk, W. Oliver. *Source Readings in Music History, the Baroque Era*. New York: W. W. Norton, 1965.

Strunk, W. Oliver. *Source Readings in Music History, the Renaissance*. New York: W.W. Norton, 1965.

Syndram, Dirk. *Renaissance and Baroque Treasury Art: The Green Vault in Dresden*. Munchen: Deutscher Kunstverlag, 2004.

Tolnay, Charles De. *The Youth of Michelangelo*. Princeton: Princeton UP, 1947.

Trexler, Richard C. *Public Life in Renaissance Florence*. London: Cornell UP, 1980.

Vasari, Giorgio. *The Lives of the Artists*. Tr. George Bull. Harmondsworth, England: Penguin, 1987.

Villani, Giovanni, Rose E. Selfe, and Philip H. Wicksteed. *Villani's Chronicle; Being Selections from the First Nine Books of the Croniche Fiorentine*. London: Archibald Constable &, 1906.

Walker, Paul R. *The Feud that Sparked the Renaissance*. New York: HarperCollins, 2004.

Winspeare, Massimo. *The Medici: The Golden Age of Collecting*. Livorno: Sillabe, 2000.

Wold, Milo, Gary Martin, James Miller, and Edmund Cykler. *Music and Art in the Western World*. McGraw Hill, 1996.

Florence Trip notes

Florence Trip notes

Florence Trip notes

Florence Trip notes

Florence Trip notes

Florence Trip notes

Florence Trip notes

Florence Trip notes

Florence Trip notes

Florence Trip notes